1969

VERY BASIC)
OLD (1969)
BUT SOME USEFUL
INFO
16-20
ENC pp 26-31
ETC

The Practical Handbook of

ELECTRICAL
REPAIRS

By Richard Day

Arco Publishing Company, Inc.
219 Park Avenue South
New York, N.Y. 10003

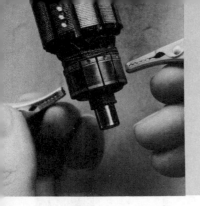
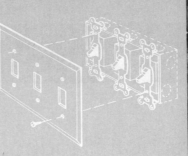

LARRY EISINGER: *Editor-in-Chief*

GEORGE TILTON: *Executive Editor*

SILVIO LEMBO: *Creative Director* • HAROLD E. PRICE: *Associate Director*

FRANK BOWERS: *Editor*

ELAINE SAPOFF: *Production Editor* • ALAINE TROW: *Production Assistant*

Editorial Staff: JOE PIAZZA, DAN BLUE, RAY GILL,
ELLENE SAUNDERS, PAMELA RIDDLE,
AMY MORRIS: *Editorial Assistant*

Art Staff: MIKE GAYNOR, ALEX SANTIAGO, JOHN SELVAGGIO,
HERBERT JONAS, JOHN CERVASIO, JACK LA CERRA

How-To Art by Henry Clark and Bruce Aldridge
Cover Color by Richard Day

Printed in U.S.A. by
FAWCETT-HAYNES PRINTING CORPORATION
Rockville, Maryland

© 1969

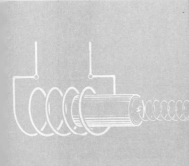
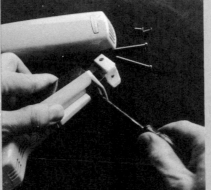
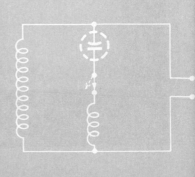

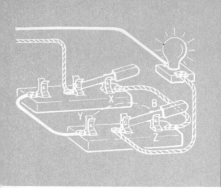

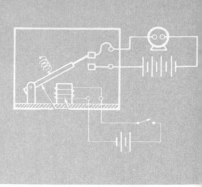

CONTENTS

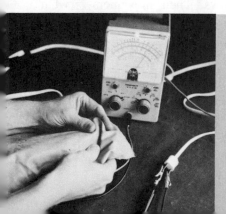

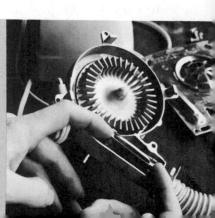

This meter reading indicates 8188 kilowatt hours on dials (left to right). Subtracting previous reading will give you the amount of electric power consumed between readings.

ELECTRICITY IS PREDICTABLE

Current follows a fascinating route from power source to your home

Electricity is fascinating. You can never learn all there is to know about it. But you don't need to know all about electricity to install wiring or to repair appliances. You need only to learn a few basics. You may already know them from high school science courses.

Electricity is brought into our homes to supply light, heat and power. The power takes the form of such jobs as drilling holes in wood, mixing batter for a cake and amplifying weak signals into sound and pictures through a television set. Electricity lets huge quantities of power, produced miles away in a generating plant, be transported near your home, divided among you and your neighbors and be converted back to power again

within your home. Light and heat are forms of power.

As you know, electricity travels through relatively large wires or cables to get to your house. Once inside, it is still carried around the house through wires, but smaller ones. Billions of electrons inside the wires move when electricity flows. Their movement is what produces the effect we call electricity.

FLOW OF ELECTRONS

Electrons are pushed out one side of the wiring in a power company's generator, which creates the electricity. They must flow back into the other side. Electrons originate in matter. All matter contains them as the smallest parts of the atoms of which all matter is made. The need for a flow of electrons is the basis of the electric circuit. If electrons left the generator but didn't return, the generator would do the greatest disappearing act ever. There is a "go" but there must also be a "come back." It's the name of the electricity game.

Think of an electric circuit as weekend highway traffic around a big city. If a bridge is out, there can be no flow of traffic. Unless a light or appliance is turned on or plugged in, there can be no current flow. The circuit is open, incomplete. When you plug in the toaster or throw on a light switch, the circuit is completed and electricity flows. It flows from the power station to your house, through the light or toaster and back to the generating station again. The flow of electrons is called a current.

Electrons can flow through a vacuum, a gas, a liquid or through solid materials. All of these resist electron flow. Some resist more than others. Glass, wood, porcelain and paper resist so well that electricity will not flow through them for all practical purposes. High resistance materials are called *insulators*. Low resistance materials are called *conductors*. They're mostly metals. Silver and copper have the lowest resistances of all metal.

NEEDS SPACE

Electricity further acts like highway traffic. Traffic on a big four-lane divided Interstate highway flows swiftly and in large quantities to and from the city without much fuss. Easily 100,000 cars can go by one spot in a day. But traffic on a narrow two-lane road backs up for miles causing much fuming, fussing and engine overheating. With all that energy only 30,000 cars may get by in a day. Electricity acts the same way in a wire, the most common conductor for it. A pencil-sized wire can pass lots of electrons without sweat. But a hair-sized wire offers much resistance to current.

Wire length as well as wire diameter has an effect. A long wire resists the flow

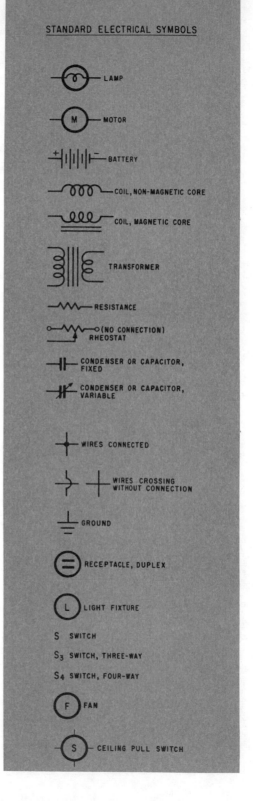

STANDARD ELECTRICAL SYMBOLS

LAMP

MOTOR

BATTERY

COIL, NON-MAGNETIC CORE

COIL, MAGNETIC CORE

TRANSFORMER

RESISTANCE

(NO CONNECTION)
RHEOSTAT

CONDENSER OR CAPACITOR, FIXED

CONDENSER OR CAPACITOR, VARIABLE

WIRES CONNECTED

WIRES CROSSING WITHOUT CONNECTION

GROUND

RECEPTACLE, DUPLEX

LIGHT FIXTURE

S   SWITCH

S_3 SWITCH, THREE-WAY

S_4 SWITCH, FOUR-WAY

FAN

CEILING PULL SWITCH

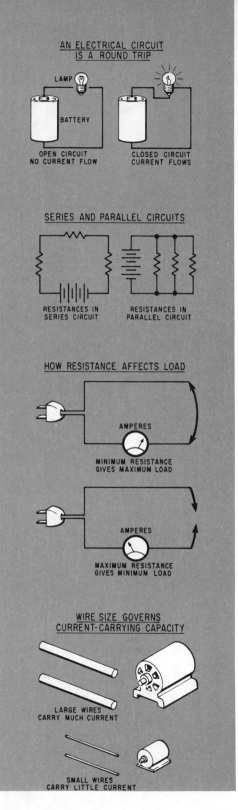

AN ELECTRICAL CIRCUIT
IS A ROUND TRIP

LAMP

BATTERY

OPEN CIRCUIT
NO CURRENT FLOW

CLOSED CIRCUIT
CURRENT FLOWS

SERIES AND PARALLEL CIRCUITS

RESISTANCES IN
SERIES CIRCUIT

RESISTANCES IN
PARALLEL CIRCUIT

HOW RESISTANCE AFFECTS LOAD

AMPERES

MINIMUM RESISTANCE
GIVES MAXIMUM LOAD

AMPERES

MAXIMUM RESISTANCE
GIVES MINIMUM LOAD

WIRE SIZE GOVERNS
CURRENT-CARRYING CAPACITY

LARGE WIRES
CARRY MUCH CURRENT

SMALL WIRES
CARRY LITTLE CURRENT

more than a short wire simply because the electricity has farther to go — like on a long highway trip some drivers tire and stop to rest. A steel wire resists more than a copper wire — much like a gravel road resists traffic more than a concrete road. While silver is an excellent conductor, you don't need three guesses why it isn't used much for wiring. Copper and more recently aluminum are the big metals in wires.

USING RESISTANCE

Normally electrical resistance is something to be minimized as much as possible. Not so, where heat is desired. Electrical resistance creates heat. Your toaster, waffle iron, bathroom heater and the like purposely put resistance in the way of electron flow to create heat. Heating devices generally use nickel-chromium wire to resist the flow of electricity while at the same time resist corrosion.

A light bulb's filament offers much resistance too, thus creating heat. But it uses the heat to make the filament glow brightly. The filament gives off some heat but more importantly, light.

Electrical resistance is measured in terms of ohms. The higher the resistance, the more ohms.

An electrical fuse located within the circuit makes good use of the principle of resistance heating. When too much current flows, the small metal conductor gets so hot it melts, breaking the circuit. The flow stops. Without a fuse in the circuit, enough electricity could flow through house wires to overheat them and start a fire.

To make current flow through a resistance it takes push, like drivers stepping on the gas. But this push takes the form of electrical pressure and is called *voltage*. Voltage is always stated as the difference, in volts, between one electrical pressure or potential and another. The potential most often used as a reference is called "ground." Ground is a numerical level of zero, not necessarily, but usually actual ground itself. The ground in a radio can be the radio's chassis. The

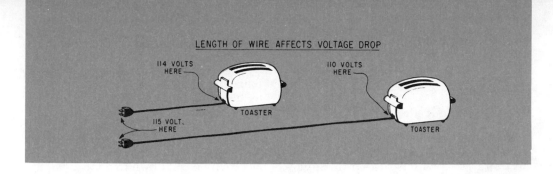

114 VOLTS
HERE

110 VOLTS
HERE

TOASTER

115 VOLT.
HERE

TOASTER

ground in your house is often a metal water pipe that travels underground.

CURRENT FLOW

You'll want to be familiar with one more electrical term—the *ampere*. Actual electrical flow is designated in amperes. One ampere of current is the passing of 6,280,000,000,000,000,000 electrons in one second. That's a lot. An average-sized household bulb draws a bit less than one ampere of flow. A household hand iron takes about 10 amps, as they're nicknamed.

Because amperage is rate of flow and voltage is pressure behind that flow, multiplying amperes times volts gives another electrical measurement that tells the amount of electricity flowing. This is called *watts*. Wattage is the electricity's ability to do work—to light lamps, to spin motors, to heat your home, or whatever. One horsepower is the same as 746 watts. An electric iron that draws 10 amperes of 120-volt juice consumes 10× 120, or 1200 watts of power. If this goes on for a whole hour, the iron will have used up 1200 *watt-hours* of electricity. And here's still another term: your electric bill is figured in *kilowatt-hours,* which is 1000 watt-hours. The iron uses 1.2 kilowatt-hours of electricity. If you pay 5 cents per kilowatt-hour for electricity, the cost of one hour's iron operation would be 1.2×5 or 6 cents.

Here are the electrical terms again: ohm—resistance; volt—pressure; ampere—flow; watt—power; and kilowatt-hour—quantity of power.

CURRENT DIRECTION

Picture the traffic on a two-lane high-

way if every minute all the cars in both directions stopped, then drove backward for one minute, then stopped and drove forward again. You might call this alternating traffic. Well, electricity supplied in nearly all homes these days is alternating current, abbreviated *AC*. This simply means that current flows first one way through the circuit, then the opposite way. Most AC makes a complete cycle both ways 60 times a second. This is called 60-cycle AC.

The other kind of current, formerly used in homes, is called *direct current,* or *DC*. Direct current always flows in one direction. Current from a car or flashlight battery is direct current.

The reason for the widespread use of AC involves the principle of electromagnetism. Electricity flowing through a wire creates magnetic lines of force around the wire. If you lay a sheet of paper over a magnet and sprinkle iron filings on it, you can see the direction

Most modern electric meters are watt-hour meters that measure the quantity of power flowing through them like a pump does fuel.

that the lines of force take. Magnetic lines of force forming around a current-carrying wire make the basis of electromagnetism.

MAGNETIC FIELDS

Just as magnetism is created by electricity, electricity can be created by magnetism. As a wire is drawn through a magnetic field, an electric current is created in that wire. The same effect is produced if the magnetic field is moved past the wire. Transformers will work on alternating current because the back-and-forth flow in the primary, or incoming, circuit creates a constantly expanding and collapsing magnetic field. These magnetic lines of force, moving in and out, cutting across wires in the secondary or outgoing circuit, create electricity in them. All the wires are coiled around a soft iron bar.

By using a smaller number of coils in the primary windings of a transformer than in the secondary windings, the voltage is stepped up. In that case the amperage is stepped down. When voltage is increased, amperage is decreased. This takes more wires in the primary winding and fewer in its secondary windings. Volts times amps on both sides of the transformer are about the same, though a small amount of power is lost in transformer heating.

This is how a transformer works to make high-voltage electricity, sometimes as much as 300,000 volts and more, for sending electric power over long distances. The high voltage overcomes the high resistance of long transmission wires. Then on arrival, the high-voltage electricity is cut down to a lower voltage by another transformer.

Direct current doesn't produce the constantly expanding and collapsing magnetic field around its wires. Therefore it isn't so easily manipulated to raise and lower voltage. DC is disappearing as power for homes.

MOTORS

The electromagnetic effects of electricity are used to advantage in electric motors as well as in transformers. Coils of wire around iron bars form powerful electromagnets inside every motor. Magnetic fields are thus induced inside the motor. In various ways they are made to rotate. The revolving part of the motor — the armature — follows like a greyhound chasing a rabbit, always a bit behind. Different types of motors work differently, but the effect is to convert electric power into mechanical power through electro-

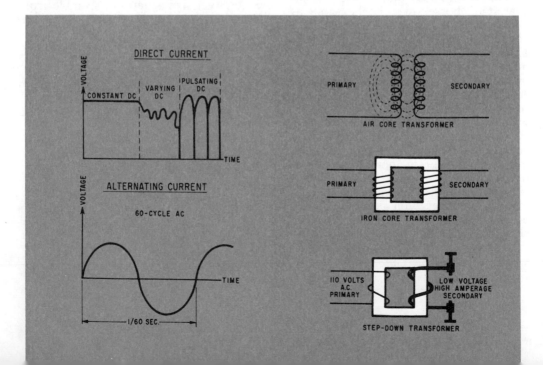

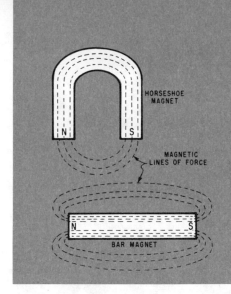

HORSESHOE MAGNET

MAGNETIC LINES OF FORCE

N   S

N _____ S

BAR MAGNET

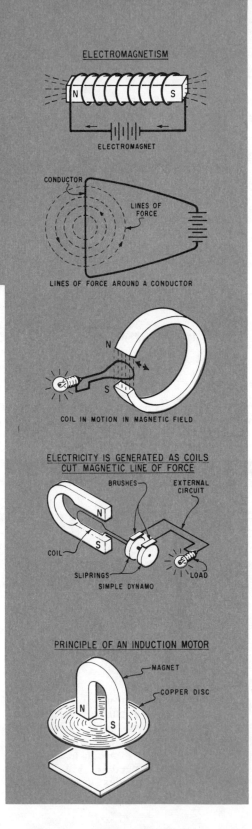

N   S

ELECTROMAGNET

CONDUCTOR

LINES OF FORCE

LINES OF FORCE AROUND A CONDUCTOR

N

S

COIL IN MOTION IN MAGNETIC FIELD

ELECTRICITY IS GENERATED AS COILS CUT MAGNETIC LINE OF FORCE

BRUSHES   EXTERNAL CIRCUIT

N

S

COIL

SLIPRINGS   LOAD

SIMPLE DYNAMO

PRINCIPLE OF AN INDUCTION MOTOR

MAGNET

COPPER DISC

N   S

magnetism. The process is highly effective.

An electric generator—or *alternator*, as an AC generator is called—converts mechanical power into electric power. In so doing, many coils of wire are rotated through an electromagnetic field, cutting the lines of force as they go. This produces a current in them. The current is lead away through wires.

Motors, transformers and generators all have helpful dispositions. When not much is being demanded of them, they don't demand much in return. For instance, an electric train transformer uses almost no power when the train is not running. When you start the train and load the transformer's secondary winding, its primary winding draws more juice, too. The same with an electric motor. An idling saw motor draws little power. When you feed a piece of wood into the saw, the current flow increases immediately. Likewise, an alternator soaks up little power from whatever is driving it until an electrical load is applied to the circuit connected to the alternator. Then it requires more power to turn it.

Principle of an induction motor: When magnetic field is rotated, copper disc, even though nonmagnetic, turns by means of eddy currents induced in it. Disc turns at a slower speed than the magnetic field. This, in essence, is how induction motor works.

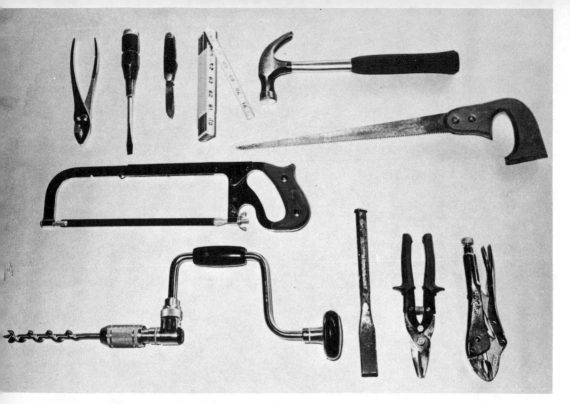

BASIC TOOLS: Pliers, screwdriver, knife, 6-foot folding rule, hammer, hacksaw, key-hole saw, brace and augur bits, electrician's all-metal chisel, metal snips and locking pliers all contribute to help you to perform basic jobs in electrical work.

ELECTRICAL TOOLS AND EQUIPMENT

Start with the basics and progress

to the power and specialized ones

Getting the right tools to do an electric wiring or repair job is half the fun. If you have done much work around the house, you probably already have most of the tools. You can acquire the others as they're needed. A full kit of electrical tools includes items in four classes: basic tools, specialized tools, power tools and electrical testing equipment. The basic tools are the ones you probably now have. You may even now own some of the others, too.

BASIC TOOLS

Pliers — a pair of 6-inch or 8-inch slip-joint pliers comes in handy for handling all manner of electrical devices, wires and appliances. You can accomplish much with no more than a pair of pliers and a screwdriver. Chances are, you already have a good pair of pliers. Right?

Screwdriver — you likely have a screwdriver, too. Almost any size will do, just so it isn't too big to handle the small screw on a receptacle cover plate. It should be sturdy, too, to use in tightening locknuts on cable connectors. Keep the point well sharpened with its faces almost parallel. A dull or improperly sharpened screwdriver is likely to slip out of a screw slot when you have to bear down on a rusted appliance screw. Better yet would be a set of several sizes of screwdrivers, including several Phillips-head types. Some appliances are put together with Phillips screws. A No. 2 Phillips is the largest size you'll need.

Knife—a knife for electrical work can be a utility knife, a paring knife stolen from the kitchen, or a pocketknife. It is used for removing insulation from the ends of wires and cables. The blade should be sharp so you don't have to force. The pocketknife is the easiest to carry around on the job.

Rule—when doing house wiring you need a method of measuring for electrical outlets and for the wires and cables to serve them. The handiest rule is a six-foot wood folding rule. It will support itself when making horizontal measurements. If you have a steel tape, don't worry. With a little support from your hand, it will do the same measuring job.

HAMMER, SAW, CHISEL

Hammer—a claw hammer is useful in wiring work. Use it for jobs such as nailing electrical boxes, tightening cable connections and chiseling out wood structural members to pass the wires.

Saws—you'll need two saws for doing electrical work, one for cutting holes in the wall and another for sawing cables and other metal devices. A keyhole saw does the wall-opening job best, the smaller the better. In its place you can use a broken hacksaw blade with one end taped for a handle. Use a regular hacksaw for cutting metal. Since the parts you'll be sawing into are mostly of thin section, fit it with a 32-tooth blade.

Chisel—the chisel is used for notching wood framing members when running wires across them. You can use a carpenter's chisel with wood or plastic handle. An all-metal electrician's chisel is

SPECIALIZED TOOLS: Electrician's side-cutting pliers, diagonal cutting pliers, long-nose pliers, end-cutting pliers, electrician's screwdriver, automatic-return screwdriver, wire-stripping tool, terminal crimping tool, set of nut-runners and pop-rivet tool together all help you to do all your electrical work both better and with ease.

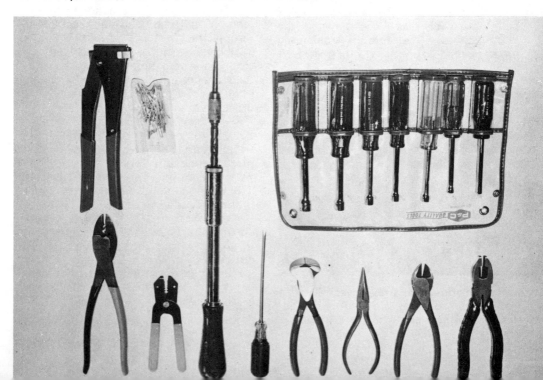

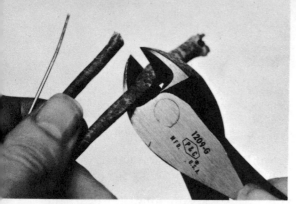

The cutters on a pair of diagonal-cutting pliers are exposed. They are therefore quite easy to use when doing wire work.

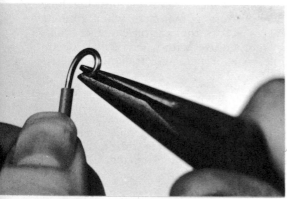

Long-nose pliers, like those shown in the photograph, are invaluable for forming the loops needed in installing wiring devices.

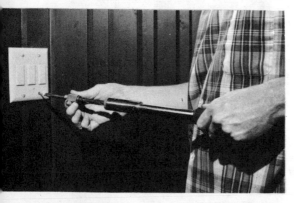

An automatic-return screwdriver, like this Stanley above, saves a lot of wrist action in finished electrical work at home.

better. Its handle won't be damaged by hard pounding.

Brace and bit — when running electrical wiring through the walls of a house, you'll need some means of boring holes for the wires, mostly of ⅝-inch diameter. A brace and bit will do the job. If you have many holes to bore, you'll want an easier method. More on that later.

Metal snips — you can get along without metal snips, but they can come in handy at times for cutting wires, armored cables, and for working with sheet metal.

Locking pliers — also in the category of handy-at-times is the locking plier/wrench. Tough holding and turning jobs in appliance repair or wiring are eased with a pair of these.

SPECIALIZED TOOLS

Electrician's pliers — you can do all sorts of electrical work without a pair of electrician's pliers, also called *side-cutters*, but you'll find them useful if you have much wiring to do. There are various sizes. Get small ones. A pair of flat gripping jaws is combined with side-cutters for cutting, stripping and splicing wires. Because cutters prevent the jaws from fully closing, electrician's pliers aren't much good for handling thin objects. You'll still need your regular slip-joint pliers.

Diagonal-cutters — where it's only cutting you want, choose these. A pair of diagonal cutters in one pocket and a pair of slip-joint pliers in the other will handle most of your plier requirements.

Long-nose pliers — another plier you'll need if you're to do much installation of switches and receptacles is the long-nose plier. Sometimes these are combined with side-cutters for doing that job, too. The long, round nose lets you form loops in the ends of wires.

End-cutters — like side-cutters, end-cutting pliers can handle the cutting jobs in wiring work. They're usually able to cut heavier wires because of their stronger construction. On the other hand, end-cutters are not as easy to use as diagonal-cutters.

Electrician's screwdriver — an electrician's screwdriver is made with the head as small as the shank for reaching into tight quarters. Get one if you need it.

A REAL WRIST-SAVER

Automatic-return screwdriver — don't be without an automatic-return screwdriver for doing much wiring. It can be a real wrist-saver when running in screws in outlet boxes, installing new receptacles and switches. It has lots of other uses around the home, too. Various sizes are available. Small is easiest to handle. This tool is also called a *Yankee* screwdriver, a trade name.

Wire-stripper — not a circus performer, this is a tool. You'll want it for extension home wiring merely as a convenience. It saves time and effort in removing the insulation from wires and does a neater job than you'll care to do with a knife. There are different sizes and types of wire-strippers. Get the kind designed for the cable type and sizes you'll be installing.

Crimping tool — this tool installs those neat looking terminals you see on appliance wiring. It's nice to have for appliance repair work.

Pop-riveting tool — often the rivets have to be removed when dismantling a small appliance. A pop-riveter is great for replacing them. Otherwise you can use bolts or screws.

Nut-runners — if you have lots of small home appliances and plan to tackle most of their repairs yourself, get a set of nut-runners. They can be purchased in a set or singly, by size. Each has a socket on the end and a screwdriver-like handle. You can get nut-runners in steps from ⅛ inch to ½ inch. Most useful are ⅜ inch and smaller.

CONDUIT TOOLS

Only if you plan to install your wiring in conduit will you need the following tools.

Conduit bender — a conduit bender is the tool to use in making bends in conduit. A length of ¾-inch pipe usually serves for a handle. Another similar tool

Once you use an inexpensive wire-stripper to bare the ends of wires, you will be so satisfied that you'll never be without one.

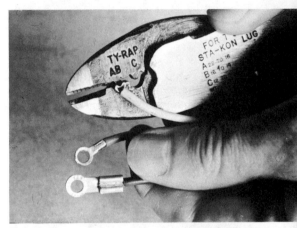

Pigtails on appliance cords sometimes call for metal terminals. A crimping tool such as this one will help you to install them.

If you are planning to do a great deal of appliance repair, get a set of nut-runners. The sockets remove nuts easily and quickly.

For working with conduit properly, you will need both a conduit bender and a length of fish tape. Bender also takes a pipe handle.

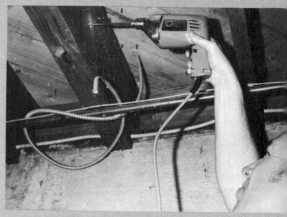

Cables running through joists and studs call for drilling of ⅝" holes. A Black and Decker electric drill can do the job.

To bend conduit smoothly you simply have to hook the tool over it on exactly the right spot near one end of conduit and then pry.

Power tools to use for electrical work include (from top to bottom) a soldering iron and gun, a ¼" drill and a saber saw.

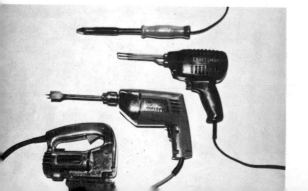

called a *pipe hickey* can be used, but smooth bends are easier with a conduit bender.

Reamer—a tapered pipe reamer is for removing the burrs left on the inside of conduit after cutting. A round file will work, too. If left, the burrs might cut through insulation on the wires.

Fish tape—that's what it's called, a fish tape. Used for fishing wires through conduit, it has a hook at one end to grip the wires. You must have it for conduit work. The tape is pushed, snaked, cajoled into a run of conduit. Then the wires for that run are attached and pulled into the run as the fish tape is pulled out.

POWER TOOLS

Electric drill—for home addition or vacation house wiring, a ¼-inch electric drill is a necessity. So many small holes are needed for wiring runs that a drill more than pays its way. You can get three types of bits for use with it. The simplest are the spade bits. Better are the rotary cutters. Best for real production hole-drilling is a standard auger bit with its shank cut off. Chuck it in a drill (½-inch, not ¼-inch) and away you go. The auger's screw threads pull it through the wood with little effort.

Saber-saw—once in a while you run

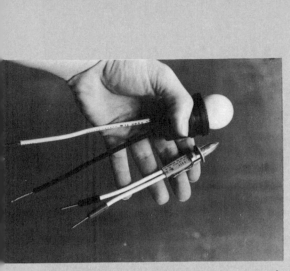

Two types of test lights. One at top is made from a rubber weatherproof socket, lower one is a sensitive neon tube type.

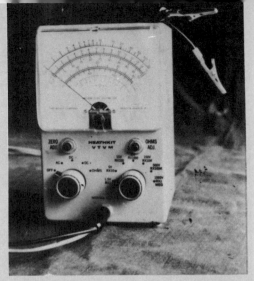

Volt-ohm meter is thoroughly reliable for troubleshooting electrical systems. It can actually make the work a lot of fun.

into a job that can be done with a saber saw, such as cutting openings for electrical boxes. If there are many such openings to cut, it can save lots of arm effort. Maybe not enough to warrant buying one, though. Peg it as nice to have.

Soldering equipment—house wiring and appliance repair sooner or later call for the use of a soldering iron or gun. Handiest is the soldering gun because it heats almost immediately. Next handiest is the electric soldering iron. Slower heating, it will handle heavier work. With the power turned off, neither of these tools will work unless you can rig an extension cord from where the electricity is on. Without power, you'll need an external flame-heated soldering copper. You'll also need a supply of solid-core corrosion-core solder. Never use acid-core solder for electrical work. A can of paste soldering flux is needed, too.

TESTING EQUIPMENT

Test light—various kinds of test lights may be purchased. All have many uses. One is to tell whether the line is "hot" or not, whether it has any electricity in it. You can make an excellent test light from a standard weatherproof rubber light socket that has a pair of insulated wires leading away. A 7½-watt bulb

screwed into the socket becomes the testlight. When the leads are touched across a pair of "live" wires, the bulb will light. This light is good only for testing circuits with 120 volts or less. More voltage would burn out the lamp.

Another kind of test light you can buy works on voltages to 240 and more. It uses a neon glow lamp.

Test meters—there are many test meters for any price you want to pay. A test meter has so many uses that you should have one if you are to do much electrical troubleshooting.

The most useful is the volt-ohm meter. Called a *VO meter*, this instrument's prime use is for testing circuit resistance and continuity. You can get one for as little as $15. They're available in kit form too. The best ones provide a number of scales, selected with a multiple-position switch. An open circuit shows up as having infinitely high resistance. A short-circuit shows as no resistance. The meter contains batteries that provide their own juice. Some also plug into an outlet.

Besides continuity checks, a VO meter can test AC and DC voltages. Thus you can check your house voltage at any location to see whether it's what it should be, as well as make other useful voltage tests.

MEET THESE WIRES AND WIRING DEVICES

Wire must never become exposed where it could cause shock or fire

Modern wires and wiring devices make it easy and fun to do your own wiring. Everything is designed to work together for ease, efficiency and safety. The basis of it all is that electrical wiring must not become exposed at any point where it could cause a shock, a short-circuit or a fire. The current-carrying metal wires are encased in insulation. That, in turn, is further encased to make it safe for use when buried in the walls of your home. All wiring and wiring devices

that you buy should bear the Underwriters Laboratories label, sometimes often merely *UL*. This signifies that they meet at least minimum standards set down for quality and safety.

Splices and joints in electric wiring must be made inside of what are termed *boxes*. Whether they're made of metal, plastic or porcelain, the boxes' function is to protect wire ends. Boxes also make wiring connections accessible inside the house. Every box, therefore, must be

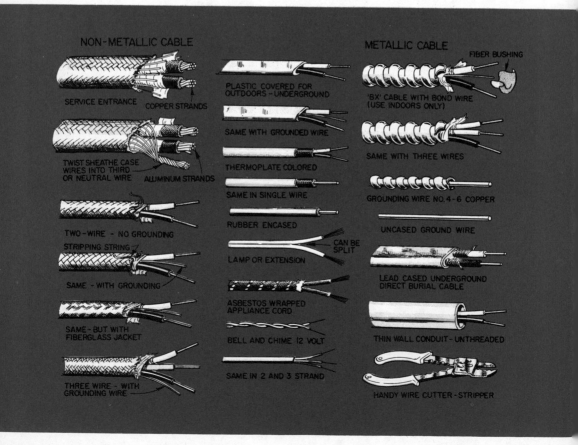

NON-METALLIC CABLE

SERVICE ENTRANCE   COPPER STRANDS

TWIST SHEATHE CASE WIRES INTO THIRD OR NEUTRAL WIRE   ALUMINUM STRANDS

TWO-WIRE - NO GROUNDING

STRIPPING STRING

SAME - WITH GROUNDING

SAME - BUT WITH FIBERGLASS JACKET

THREE WIRE - WITH GROUNDING WIRE

PLASTIC COVERED FOR OUTDOORS - UNDERGROUND

SAME WITH GROUNDED WIRE

THERMOPLATE COLORED

SAME IN SINGLE WIRE

RUBBER ENCASED

CAN BE SPLIT

LAMP OR EXTENSION

ASBESTOS WRAPPED APPLIANCE CORD

BELL AND CHIME 12 VOLT

SAME IN 2 AND 3 STRAND

METALLIC CABLE

FIBER BUSHING

'BX' CABLE WITH BOND WIRE (USE INDOORS ONLY)

SAME WITH THREE WIRES

GROUNDING WIRE NO. 4-6 COPPER

UNCASED GROUND WIRE

LEAD CASED UNDERGROUND DIRECT BURIAL CABLE

THIN WALL CONDUIT - UNTHREADED

HANDY WIRE CUTTER - STRIPPER

placed so that its wiring will be permanently accessible. All wire runs must be continuous from box to box. No splices may be made outside a box. Boxes are called *switch boxes, outlet boxes, fixture boxes* or *junction boxes*, depending on their use.

CHOOSING THE WIRE

Wiring that runs inside the walls of a house is called cable or *run*. A *run* is a length of wiring between two boxes. Cable can be any of three types depending on what the local code permits: Nonmetallic cable, armored cable or conduit. Conduit is used only in new work or in extending old work. The other two types are used in both new construction and for remodeling. Before you get down to selecting one or the other, find out what types your building code will let you use.

The conductors in all wiring must be color-coded. Every house wiring cable has a white wire and a black wire. Black designates the "hot" current-carrying wire. White designates the neutral current-carrying wire that should be at or near ground potential. Three-wire cable also contains a red current-carrying wire designating a second "hot" wire.

In addition to these wires, cable often carries a smaller bare wire that does not usually carry electricity, but is grounded. This wire provides a safe path for wayward electricity if a "hot" wire should become exposed and contact the body of an appliance or a metal electrical box. The bare wire provides a ground continuity for every circuit.

Wires used in conduit runs follow the same color coding. No bare wire is needed because the conduit itself is so well grounded.

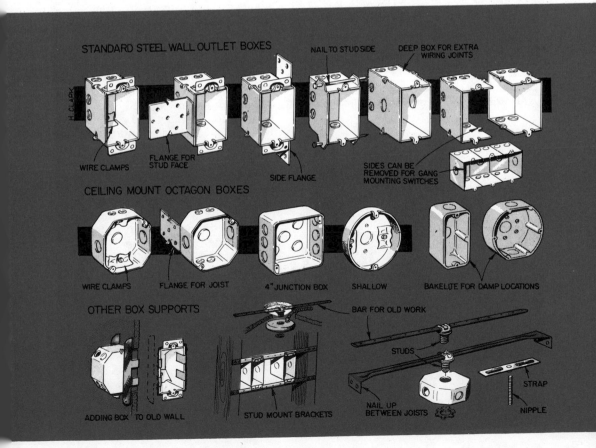

STANDARD STEEL WALL OUTLET BOXES — NAIL TO STUD SIDE — DEEP BOX FOR EXTRA WIRING JOINTS

WIRE CLAMPS — FLANGE FOR STUD FACE — SIDE FLANGE — SIDES CAN BE REMOVED FOR GANG MOUNTING SWITCHES

CEILING MOUNT OCTAGON BOXES

WIRE CLAMPS — FLANGE FOR JOIST — 4" JUNCTION BOX — SHALLOW — BAKELITE FOR DAMP LOCATIONS

OTHER BOX SUPPORTS — BAR FOR OLD WORK

ADDING BOX TO OLD WALL — STUD MOUNT BRACKETS — STUDS — NAIL UP BETWEEN JOISTS — STRAP — NIPPLE

Best boxes for new work are 4" square. Single-gang or two-gang reducing covers screw onto box and reach through finished wall.

Make knockouts in boxes by hitting free end with a screwdriver and your palm or pliers. Keep a beat-up screwdriver for this use.

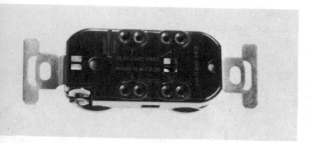

Push-in back-wired receptacle installs easily and quickly. Wires are pushed into holes.

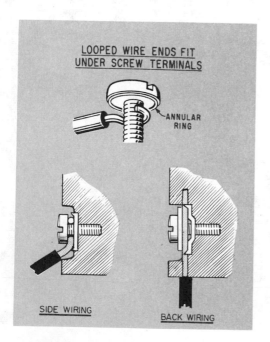

LOOPED WIRE ENDS FIT UNDER SCREW TERMINALS

ANNULAR RING

SIDE WIRING

BACK WIRING

LOW-COST CABLE

Lowest in cost is nonmetallic cable. It is widely used outside of cities. City codes are often too restricting to let you use it. Nonmetallic cable (sometimes called *Romex*, a trade name) consists of two or three insulated conductors, preferably with another uninsulated wire. These are contained in a tough plastic or impregnated woven outer sheath that can be pulled or "snaked" through walls as needed. Nonmetallic cable is usually ivory or gray in color and is easy to pull and strip. The main drawback is that it's subject to mechanical damage. Nails can penetrate it. You have to be careful to place it so that nails can't reach the cable when it's hidden in the wall.

One type of nonmetallic cable is designed for indoor use only. This is designated Type NM. A better, tougher type is designated Type NMC. It can be used outdoors. or indoors and in damp or wet locations. Type NMC also can be used in dry locations. You may run it through masonry walls and in the cores on concrete block walls. A few brands of Type NMC nonmetallic may also be buried underground if protected by a fuse or circuit breaker. Check with your supplier. NM and NMC are look-alikes, anyway. NMC is referred to by some as dual-purpose cable. Use it and you avoid the need for buying two types.

A three-wire grounding type duplex outlet is back-wired in order to let the wires be installed from behind without looped ends.

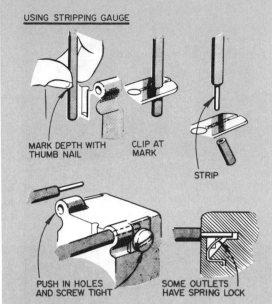

MARK DEPTH WITH THUMB NAIL

CLIP AT MARK

STRIP

PUSH IN HOLES AND SCREW TIGHT

SOME OUTLETS HAVE SPRING LOCK

TYPE UF

A third type of nonmetallic cable is designated Type UF. It can be used for fused circuits underground and for any of the uses of types NM or NMC. This is the cable to use for a run out to a driveway post lamp. Bury it directly in the ground.

Still another nonmetallic cable is Type USE, the underground service entrance cable. It need not be fused and can be attached to the power company's wires and lead to your house underground.

Nonmetallic cable may be used with metal, plastic or porcelain boxes, though for most uses metal boxes are best.

ARMORED CABLE

Flexible armored cable—often called *BX*, a brand name—is wrapped with a galvanized steel jacket that protects it from most mechanical damage. Use armored cable in dry locations only, because it is subject to corrosion. Never use armored cable outdoors or buried in the ground. As with nonmetallic cable, armored cable may be used for runs that are exposed in the wall, floor or ceiling. Armored cable may be embedded in plaster if the location is not damp. It must always be used with steel boxes. Armored cable is available as two- or

Where the length of the strip is important, the gauge on the back of the wiring device tells you how much insulation to remove.

Push-in receptacle engages wires from back as they are inserted. Special openings let you disengage them later, if necessary.

Safety-grounding duplex receptacle is designed so that current is shunted harmlessly away from an inserted metallic object.

Twist-locking receptacle accepts standard parallel-blade plus. With a slight twist to the right, you effectively lock them in.

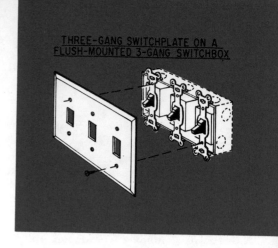

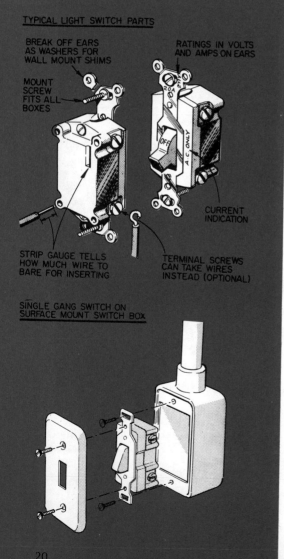

TYPICAL LIGHT SWITCH PARTS

BREAK OFF EARS AS WASHERS FOR WALL MOUNT SHIMS

RATINGS IN VOLTS AND AMPS ON EARS

MOUNT SCREW FITS ALL BOXES

OFF

A.C. ONLY

CURRENT INDICATION

STRIP GAUGE TELLS HOW MUCH WIRE TO BARE FOR INSERTING

TERMINAL SCREWS CAN TAKE WIRES INSTEAD (OPTIONAL)

SINGLE GANG SWITCH ON SURFACE MOUNT SWITCH BOX

three-wire and usually has an additional bare wire. Because of the steel covering, armored costs more than nonmetallic cable. The covering makes it a little harder to pull through the walls. Once installed it is safer from mechanical damage, though nails can penetrate it.

CONDUIT

Few will argue that the best, most flexible electrical installation, once it's in, is conduit. With conduit installations, a hollow pipe casing for the wiring is first run from box to box. Bends in the conduit are made with a bending tool. Joints are made with conduit connectors. With a little practice as well as patience you can make every bend and length come out right. Some strict local electric codes require conduit for all new work. The most used sizes for conduit in homes are ½-inch and ¾-inch.

Once all the conduit is in, wires are "fished" through the pipes to every outlet as needed. For this, single-conductor insulated wires are used. As many wires as are needed can be fished through, up to the maximum number permitted in the size of conduit used. The entire system is grounded through the conduit and the metal boxes used with it.

There are two types of conduit: thin-wall and rigid. Rigid conduit is much like water pipe, but with smoother insides to protect the wires. Rigid uses threaded fittings. Thin-wall is more economical, easier to bend and uses compression-

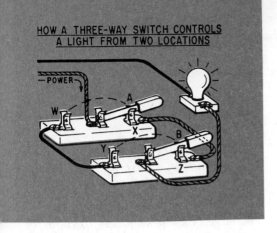

HOW A THREE-WAY SWITCH CONTROLS
A LIGHT FROM TWO LOCATIONS

Press switch works differently from common toggle switch. A push turns it on and off.

type fittings. Both are galvanized and may be used indoors or out, exposed or concealed. Rigid conduit may be buried in the ground or encased in masonry but not where it would come in contact with cinders or cinder blocks, because a corrosive reaction may develop. Conductors used in conduit are often Type T or Type TW. They're prewaxed for easier pulling through the conduit runs.

WIRES

Wire size is very important in electrical work. The conductors must be heavy enough to carry the maximum load they are intended to receive. The accepted standard is the American Wire Gauge sizes, abbreviated *AWG*. These assign numbers to the various sizes of wires. Those used in house wiring vary from No. 18 (smallest used as cords and bell wire) to No. 3/0 (largest normally found in service entrance wiring). The smallest wire used in actual house circuits is No. 14 and it is giving way to larger No. 12 wire.

Wires may be either one solid conductor or stranded. Stranded wires are many small ones formed together to make the required gauge. House circuits are wired with solid-conductor wire. Extension cords and heavy service entrance wiring is stranded to be more flexible.

Conductors are usually copper. Aluminum is making headway as a wiring material because of its light weight, lower cost and greater availability over copper.

Aluminum has less current-carrying ability than copper and the next-larger wire size must be used to handle the same load. Wiring devices, such as switches and receptacles, used with aluminum wire must be approved for it. Sometimes they are stamped "Al-Cu," the chemical terms for aluminum and copper. Other times you'll have to ask your supplier. Most of those made now are dual-metallic.

WIRING DEVICES

The broad class of accessories that go with electric wires is called wiring devices. Without them, cables would be useless. The most common wiring device is the box. There are *switch boxes, outlet boxes* (for receptacles), *fixture boxes* and *junction boxes. Junction boxes* are used when joining wires together. Made of metal, plastic or porcelain, boxes have knockouts in their sides and backs to admit the wires. Cable or conduit is fastened to the box with connectors. Some boxes have built-in clamps to take nonmetallic or armored cable. These take the place of connectors. The additional cost of a box with clamps is less than the cost of one connector. Clamps save time in wiring makeup. They serve cables coming in from two sides. Those entering at the other sides or at the back of the box need connectors. Each connector has a locknut that fits inside the box.

The front of the box faces into the

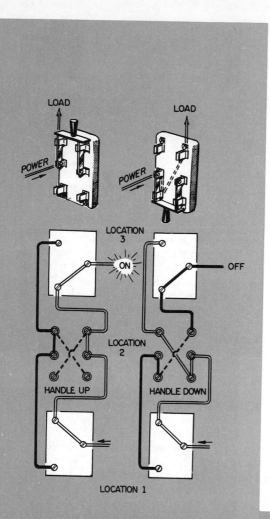

LOAD

LOAD

POWER

POWER

LOCATION 3

ON

OFF

LOCATION 2

HANDLE UP

HANDLE DOWN

LOCATION 1

room, cabinet or other permanently accessible location. It is covered by the outlet cover or fixture. If the box is merely being used to join wires, it may have a flat metal cover. Screws on the front of such a box allow the cover to be fastened firmly.

Of the many boxes, the handiest is the 4-inch-square box. Use it for switch and outlet boxes. You can get them plain or with handy self-mounting tabs. The tab is nailed directly to a framing member. The large box allows plenty of room for working with wires. You'll appreciate it when you come to that phase of the work.

Because of the large opening, the 4-inch box needs a cover to bring the wall opening down to a size that can be hidden by a switch plate or receptacle cover. For receptacles and switches use what's called a *single-gang* cover. The switch cover is always placed vertically. For receptacles you may install the cover horizontally or vertically, usually vertically. The wall material—whether plaster, plasterboard or paneling—fits around the cover, which should be flush with the finished wall surface. The cover must be designed for use with the wall thickness you are using; order them that way. Mount the box itself flush with the inside of the wall.

A four-way switch (left and at location 2) is a special double-pole double-throw switch. Used between a pair of three-way switches, it enables additional switching locations. Insulated jumpers on the back conduct power to the contacts diagonally opposite. It can thus route power either of two conductors, depending on whether the handle is up or down. Power enters the four-way from the three-way switch at the bottom. With the handle up, the four-way sends current to one contact of the upper three-way switch. Since this switch's blade is on this contact, the current flows through to the light. Turning the four-way's handle down puts out the light because the power is sent to the other contact of the three-way switch. The blade is not on this contact and the power stops there. By changing the handle of any of the three switches, the light can be turned on again. A load can be controlled from four locations by placing two four-way switches between the pair of three-way's; it can be controlled from five locations by placing three four-ways between a pair of three-ways.

OTHER OUTLET BOXES

Many other kinds of outlet boxes are made. For switches you can use the standard rectangular switch box with removable sides that let you gang two or more boxes together for multiple switches. Surface-mounted boxes have rounded edges for good looks when exposed to view. These can be screwed to the wall for use in basement wiring. Switch and outlet covers are available.

Junction boxes are octagonal and made in 4-inch and handier 3¼-inch sizes. Their covers come in many types to enable them to also be used as receptacle and fixture boxes.

The number of wires that can be used in a box is limited by code. The standard 2-¾×3×1¾-inch switch box with clamps and receptacle may contain up to five No. 12 or No. 14 wires. If you ever want to branch off from a run containing these small clamp boxes, you'll have to find the last box in the circuit, because every other box already contains four wires and can't handle two more. The last one in the run will have only two wires in it.

This points out another advantage to using 4-inch-square boxes with reducing covers: You can always add another cable without crowding.

Most outlet boxes are metal. Metal not only provides ground continuity, it also prevents accidentally drilling into the box from the opposite side of the wall, floor or ceiling. Steel boxes have partially prepunched knockouts; merely punch them out as needed, using a screwdriver and hammer. Clamp-type boxes also contain slotted knockouts that may be removed by inserting the blade of a screwdriver and prying. Always be sure before removing a knockout. You cannot put it back again, and you can't use a box with an open knockout. You can, however, snap in a device called a K.O. seal. Great box-savers.

SELF-FASTENING BOXES

For remodeling work and where you need boxes in existing walls, by all means use self-fastening boxes. These use screw clamps or bent tabs at the sides to hold them in sawed-out openings through the wall. They are useful for wiring switches and receptacles.

You can get special boxes for surface wiring, for thin walls, for cramped spaces or almost any other need you run into. Ask your dealer.

In new work the boxes are usually mounted between studs on hangers or fastened to the studs themselves. Ceiling boxes for fixtures hang from headers nailed between ceiling joists or from specially designed metal hangers. These are great. They save on carpentry. Receptacle boxes are normally located 12

Many specialized devices are available, such as this high-heat switch by Paulding.

Switched or unswitched porcelain sockets can make instant light out of open ceiling box.

The greatest way to splice wires is with solderless connectors. Shown at left is the split-bolt type for large wires. Others are self-insulating plastic types for smaller sizes of wires. The one at the far right is used mainly in cramped quarters of motors.

inches above the floor. In the kitchen they are placed at counter or table height. The same for the dining room table. Switch boxes are usually mounted about 48 inches above the floor. Be sure to get them next to the door opening on the knob side, not the hinge side. Switches at stairways should be located so you can reach them without stepping on the first step. The reason is obvious.

FINISHING DEVICES

In new construction the wiring is done before the wall materials are put on, up to the point of installing wires and boxes. After the finished wall materials are on, and often after they are painted, the finished wiring is installed, including the receptacles, switches and fixtures.

The usual receptacle is a duplex unit, serving two plugs. All new receptacles must be of the three-wire grounding type, installed in grounded metal boxes. These take regular two-prong plugs or the three-prong grounding plugs found on many portable power tools and other appliances.

Every grounding receptacle has a green grounding terminal. If the metal outlet box is flush with the finished wall so that the projecting metal tabs on the outlet make firm contact with the box, no wires need be connected to this grounding terminal. Otherwise the terminal should be wired to a screw

threaded into the back of the metal outlet box. Modern boxes have pre-threaded holes for this. Older boxes may have to be pilot-drilled and sheet metal screws driven in to secure grounding wires. Don't install a grounding receptacle that is not actually grounded. This could be dangerously misleading.

Remodeling work where the present outlet boxes are not metal or are not grounded must be fitted with the old-style two-prong convenience outlets.

Receptacles normally have screw terminals. For a little more money, you can buy the convenience of push-in terminals. With these the wires are stripped for a distance as shown by a "strip-gauge" on the receptacle. The bared ends can be pushed into holes in the holes in the back of the device. If the wires ever have to be released, separate holes are provided for pushing in a knife, wire or other instrument to loosen the grip.

OTHER RECEPTACLES

Many other receptacles are also available. Condensed receptacles, where three or more will fit into the space usually required for two, can give you extra "plug-ability." On the other extreme are single receptacles that can be used in place of duplexes. Special outlets with hangers for wall clocks also can be had. These have space to store excess cord. Safety outlets prevent children from poking things into the opening; they have caps that twist shut whenever the plug is removed, closing the openings. Dust-proof outlets are made for floor use. Some of these have rubber flaps that spring back when the plug is removed.

Outdoors you'll want to use special weatherproof receptacles with hinged or screw-on covers.

An interchangeable system lets you use a receptacle, a switch or a pilot light in the same outlet in groups up to three per outlet.

Most new duplex receptacles are of the double-breaker type. That is, they have tiny break-away tabs that electrically connect the two halves of the device. To put each half on a separate cir-

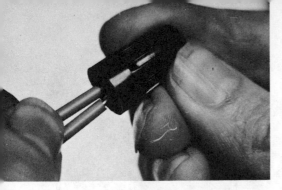

In order to install a solderless connector, it's necessary to first twist the wires together, then screw connector on over them.

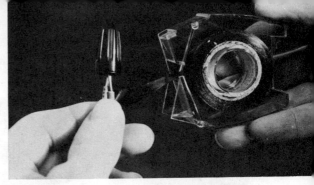

Plastic tape can cover improperly stripped wires that are exposed below a solderless connector. Better yet, snip them shorter.

cuit in what's called a "split system," you merely break away the tabs and wire the halves individually from different circuits. More about that later.

Most receptacles are side-wired. You can also get them backwired if you like. These do away with the need for forming terminal loops in wires connected to them. Simply slip the stripped wire end under the clamp and tighten the screw — it grabs. The screws are in the usual position, but press onto metal clamps which grip the wires. Two wires per screw can be accommodated. It's a terrific time-saver.

SWITCHES

Switches take many forms to meet many needs. For most residential purposes they come in single-pole single-throw, three-way and four-way. Most common is the simple single-pole single-throw switch. It usually has two terminals. One connects to the power, the other to the load. This familiar switch controls a light from one location.

A three way switch has three terminals and the handle is not lettered *on* and *off*. Use a three-way switch to control a light from two locations. When such an arrangement is used to light stairways, one switch is located at each end of the stairway.

A four-way switch has four terminals and no *on* or *off* lettering. Four-way switches are used to provide light control from any number of locations between a pair of three-way switches. How

to handle the wiring arrangements will be shown in another chapter.

You can get pilot-lighted switches that indicate when an unseen light or motor is turned on. They are convenient for switching a basement light or heating plant from upstairs. Additionally there are feather-touch switches, tap-switches, pushbutton switches and flat plate touch-switches. You even can get locking switches.

For switching a light, such as a garage light where a delayed shutoff is desirable, use a delay toggle switch. It gives you time to get in the house before the light goes off.

TIMER SWITCH

A timer switch provides the same delayed shutoff, but for longer periods. Use it for operating a bathroom or kitchen vent fan where you want the fan to run for a time but don't want to make a special trip to turn it off. Time can vary from a minute up to an hour. A "hold" position lets you run the fan continually.

Interchangeable switches can fit three to a normal switch box or be combined with other devices in the same box.

A high-low switch gives full light in the *up* position, dimmed light in the *down* position and turns off in the *middle* position. There are photoelectric switches and clock switches for special purposes.

Switch plates to cover the workings of a switch come in many designs in plastic, metal and ceramics. You even can get them electroluminescent so they light up in the dark.

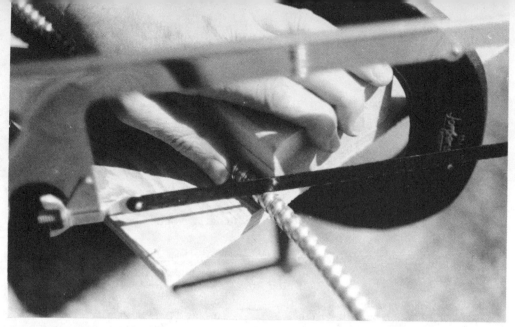

To cut an armored cable properly, you should first support it against a piece of 2 x 4 clamped to tabletop or stud. Saw at an angle across the spiral, but not too deeply.

WORKING WITH WIRE

Preparing ends of wire, cable for joining other wires and devices

The ends of wires and cables must be prepared for joining to other wires or to wiring devices. The basic steps are cutting, stripping off sheaths, installing cable in boxes, stripping insulation from the wire ends and connecting the wires as necessary.

Before you cut a cable make sure there is 8 inches extra at both ends to let you work conveniently inside the box. Nonmetallic cable can be cut easily with metal snips. One slice and you're through. When cutting cable, hacksaw through one section of the armor at an angle. Then twist the armor to snap it off. Push the armor back on both sides of the cut to get clearance for a pair of metal snips or diagonal cutters and sever the conductors inside.

Conduit is cut with a hacksaw or pipe cutter. Be sure to remove all burrs left on the inside of every length of conduit.

Use a round file or tapered reamer.

To prepare nonmetallic cable for installation in the box, slice off the outer covering with a cable-stripper or knife, exposing about 8 inches of the insulated conductors. Be careful not to nick or sever the bare wire if there is one.

CABLE CONNECTORS

When using a box without clamps, use cable connectors to join the cable to the box. One or the other is necessary to join the cable to the box. Loose cables could chafe and wear through the insulation. What's more, no ground continuity is provided by a loose cable connection. Slip a connector over the end of the cable and clamp it tight. Insert the cable through a knockout hole in the box. Install a locknut from the inside with the ears facing the box. Draw it tight, mak-

NUMBER OF CONDUCTORS IN ONE CONDUIT OR TUBING									
SIZE (AWG)	1	2	3	4	5	6	7	8	9
18	½	½	½	½	½	½	½	¾	¾
16	½	½	½	½	½	½	¾	¾	¾
14	½	½	½	½	¾	¾	1	1	1
12	½	½	½	¾	¾	1	1	1	1¼
10	½	¾	¾	¾	1	1	1	1¼	1¼
8	½	¾	¾	1	1¼	1¼	1¼	1½	1½
6	½	1	1	1¼	1½	1½	2	2	2
4	½	1¼	1¼	1½	1½	2	2	2	2½
3	¾	1¼	1¼	1½	2	2	2	2½	2½
2	¾	1¼	1¼	2	2	2	2½	2½	2½
1	¾	1½	1½	2	2½	2½	2½	3	3
0	1	1½	2	2	2½	2½	3	3	3
2/0	1	2	2	2½	2½	3	3	3	3½
3/0	1	2	2	2½	3	3	3½	3½	3½

ing the tabs dig into the metal box for a firm electrical ground connection. To turn the locknut, set a screwdriver against one of the ears and tap on the handle. Purists won't like hammering on a screwdriver, but it's the accepted way. Moreover, most electricians hammer on the screwdriver with their side-cutters. Ouch! If it bothers you, keep a special beat-up screwdriver just for this purpose.

Nonmetallic cable should be fastened with straps, not staples. Fasten it within a foot of every box and at 3-foot minimum intervals on supporting members wherever it is to be exposed along studs, joists, walls ceilings. When an exposed nonmetallic cable is run across open spaces, such as attic or basement joists, it should be fastened to a 1×2-inch wood runner that is nailed to the joists. Better yet, drill holes through each joist in the center of their width and pull the cable through the holes. There is no harm in angling these holes through the stud or joist if your drill won't fit between for a straight shot. Some attic and roof space runs require wood guard strips to protect the cable. Consult your local code.

Twist spiral halves apart to complete cut. If you're cutting the cable, nip through wire. If stripping, pull off the end armor.

LESS SUPPORT NEEDED

Nonmetallic cable in concealed locations can get by with less support. Put a cable strap every 4½ feet and within a foot of every box. In old work, in which the cable is fished through concealed spaces in wall, floor and ceiling, straps are required only in the exposed portions of the runs.

Unless you are wiring farm outbuildings without a good means of grounding the whole wiring system, all runs of nonmetallic cable should be made with cable containing a bare grounding wire. Metal boxes are usually used. The bare wire is connected to every box. Special grounding clips are available for this purpose. The bare grounding wire insures a continuously grounded electrical system.

The boxes will always be at ground potential to reduce the risk of getting shocked and to provide for the grounding of portable power tools with three-pronged grounding plugs. Where plastic or porcelain boxes are used the bare grounding wire can be attached to the green terminal of the receptacle or to the fixture for good grounding. The National Electric Code is strict on grounding. It's for your own safety. Make sure that every receptacle or fixture you install is well grounded.

PREPARING ARMORED CABLE

To strip armored cable, saw across the armor at an angle with a hacksaw, as you did to cut it. Clamp it in a vise or lay it on a bench with a block of wood clamped behind to hold it. Don't try to saw a cable while it's laid across your knee. Remove 8 inches of armor at each end. A good twist when the armor has been partially severed will separate it without sawing deeply and risking injury to the insulation. Slip off the severed armor. Slip an armored cable bushing—sometimes called an *anti-short* bushing—around the wires, between them and the armor. Always use bushing with armored cable. They protect the wires from being shorted by the sharp edge of cut armor.

Pull off the paper covering. Then slip an armored cable connector onto the end of the cable. If the cable contains a bare grounding wire (it should), first bend that back along the cable. When the connector is in place over the cable, wrap the bare wire around the connector

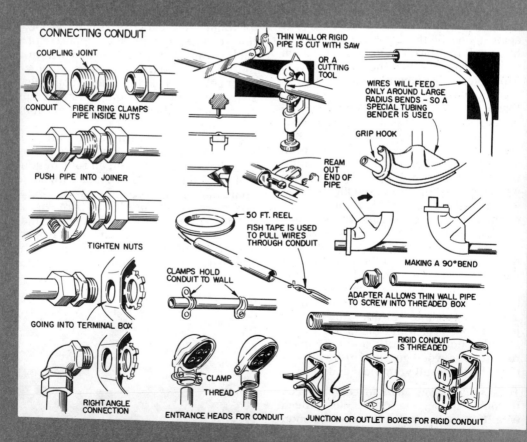

28

screw and tighten the screw. If a connection is used that has no place to fasten the bare wire, the wire should be attached to the back of the box with a screw (or to the outlet or fixture).

KNOCKOUT HOLE

With the locknut removed, the wires and connector are inserted into a knockout hole in the box and drawn securely by installing and tightening the locknut. Armored cable assures good ground continuity with the metal armor plus the bare grounding wire inside. This grounds the box back to the main ground at the service entrance (see next chapter).

Except for concealed runs in remodeling work, where you can't get at it, armored cable must be supported every 4½ feet and within a foot of every box. Either straps or staples are all right for use with armored cable.

Bends in nonmetallic cable should be to a minimum tightness of five times the diameter of the cable if the bend were continued to form a complete circle. Bends in armored cable should be a minimum of seven cable diameters. If a cable must bend tightly to enter a box, use a 90-degree cable connector.

WORKING WITH CONDUIT

Conduit is bent as needed with a conduit bender or pipe hickey. To make a 12-inch, 90-degree bend using a bender, measure 7 inches in from the end of the conduit. Hook the bender over the conduit, with the inside of the hook at the mark, and make your bend. Use one foot

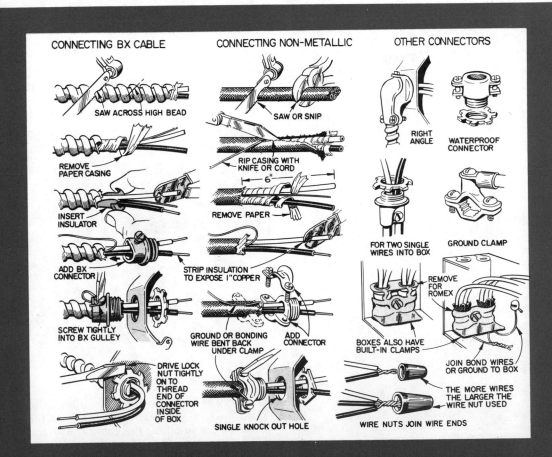

CONNECTING BX CABLE

SAW ACROSS HIGH BEAD

REMOVE PAPER CASING

INSERT INSULATOR

ADD BX CONNECTOR

SCREW TIGHTLY INTO BX GULLEY

DRIVE LOCK NUT TIGHTLY ON TO THREAD END OF CONNECTOR INSIDE OF BOX

CONNECTING NON-METALLIC

SAW OR SNIP

RIP CASING WITH KNIFE OR CORD

6"

REMOVE PAPER

STRIP INSULATION TO EXPOSE 1" COPPER

GROUND OR BONDING WIRE BENT BACK UNDER CLAMP

ADD CONNECTOR

SINGLE KNOCK OUT HOLE

OTHER CONNECTORS

RIGHT ANGLE

WATERPROOF CONNECTOR

FOR TWO SINGLE WIRES INTO BOX

GROUND CLAMP

REMOVE FOR ROMEX

BOXES ALSO HAVE BUILT-IN CLAMPS

JOIN BOND WIRES OR GROUND TO BOX

THE MORE WIRES THE LARGER THE WIRE NUT USED

WIRE NUTS JOIN WIRE ENDS

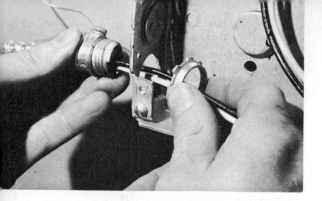

Install armored cable bushing and connector over end of stripped cable. Insert cable into a handy box knockout with locknut inside.

Pound screwdriver against the ears to tighten locknut. To make a sound electrical connection, locknut should dig into metal box.

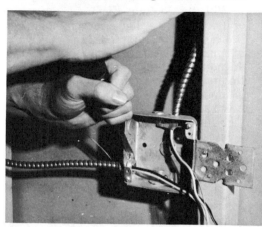

Below, strap or staple cable within 12" of every box and every 4½' in other locations. No staples on nonmetallic cable; they cut!

Remove insulation from wire ends with sharp knife, if you don't have wire-stripper. Remember not to "ring" wire. Cut at an angle.

One way of grounding to a metal box is to bend the bare grounding wire back on the cable before installing the cable connector.

to hold the conduit as you bend. The difference between 12 inches and 7 inches is called "take-up." This length is needed to go around the bend. Only four 90-degree bends are permitted by Code in any single run of conduit (between two boxes). This is so that wire-pulling will not be so tough as to strip off the insulation. Generally all the wires in a run are pulled into it at once. Short runs can be pushed in by hand. Long runs are pulled with a fish tape.

CONNECTIONS

When you're ready to splice wires and connect them to wiring devices, strip off a half-inch of insulation from each end of every wire. Sometimes a strip gauge is included on the back of the wiring device. Use it as a guide.

When stripping insulation from wires, hold the knife at an angle to the wire and slice off the rubber or plastic covering as though you were sharpening a pencil. Never cut around the wire. This makes square shoulders, but may nick the wire so much it is apt to break off later.

All wires that are to be joined should be bright and clean. Scrape them with the back of your knife blade.

Make all splices inside the box using solderless connectors. Use one size for Nos. 14 to 18 wire; another for No. 12, still another for No. 10. Where three or more wires are spliced together, you may need to use the next-larger size solderless connector. Different-sized wires may be spliced in the same connector.

SPLICING WIRE

If there are more wires than can be spliced conveniently in one connector, say four wires, splice two of them with a 3-inch lead wire. Then splice the lead wire with the other two. With the use of solderless connectors you may never have to solder and tape a connection. If any uninsulated wire sticks out of the connector after you have tightened it, remove the connector, clip off some excess wire and reinstall it. Or you can wrap plastic electrical tape around the bare area.

Splices and taps made without solderless connectors must be soldered and taped. The finished connection must be as well insulated with tape as the wires themselves.

Connections to screw terminals of switches and receptacles should be made with the ends of each wire bent into a loop. Each loop should lie clockwise in the same direction the screw turns to tighten. This tends to pull the loop in, rather than loosen it. Back-wired devices accept straight wire ends. Looping is not needed with them.

Large wires, such as those feeding your house from the main power lines, are joined with split-bolt solderless connectors. These are not self-insulating and must be taped after they're installed.

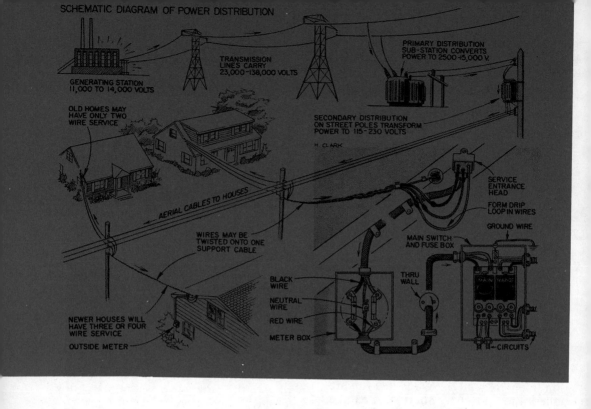

GENERATING STATION
11,000 TO 14,000 VOLTS

OLD HOMES MAY
HAVE ONLY TWO
WIRE SERVICE

TRANSMISSION
LINES CARRY
23,000-138,000 VOLTS

PRIMARY DISTRIBUTION
SUB-STATION CONVERTS
POWER TO 2500-15,000 V.

SECONDARY DISTRIBUTION
ON STREET POLES TRANSFORM
POWER TO 115-230 VOLTS

H. CLARK

AERIAL CABLES TO HOUSES

WIRES MAY BE
TWISTED ONTO ONE
SUPPORT CABLE

SERVICE
ENTRANCE
HEAD

FORM DRIP
LOOP IN WIRES

GROUND WIRE

MAIN SWITCH
AND FUSE BOX

THRU
WALL

BLACK
WIRE

NEUTRAL
WIRE

RED WIRE

METER BOX

NEWER HOUSES WILL
HAVE THREE OR FOUR
WIRE SERVICE

OUTSIDE METER

CIRCUITS

HOW YOUR HOUSE IS WIRED

A well-wired house provides circuits for present and future needs

All house wiring consists of these components: power lines, service entrance, meter, service panel with over-current devices (fuses, circuit breakers), and house circuits. Since local electrical codes vary considerably, systems around the nation are not all exactly alike. Basically they are, though.

The beginning of the house wiring system is the point where your house power lines attach to the power company's lines at the top of the pole. From there the lines are run either overhead or underground to a convenient point on your house. The nicest, most modern service enters below ground.

Most house service entrance wiring uses either two or three wires. Having just two wires tells you that your house receives only 120-volt power, way under-wired for today's many needs.

Two wires comprise (1) a neutral wire, which is sometimes uninsulated, and (2) a "hot" wire, which is always insulated. The electric potential across the two is 120 volts, or close to it. The neutral is a current-carrying wire, even though it's grounded at the house entrance and often at the utility pole. Always treat it as such.

THREE WIRES GOOD

If your house has three entrance wires, it's a good sign. They provide 120-140-volt power. One wire is a neutral wire. The others are "hot" wires. The electric potential from either "hot" wire to the neutral wire is 120 volts. The potential

HOUSE CIRCUITS

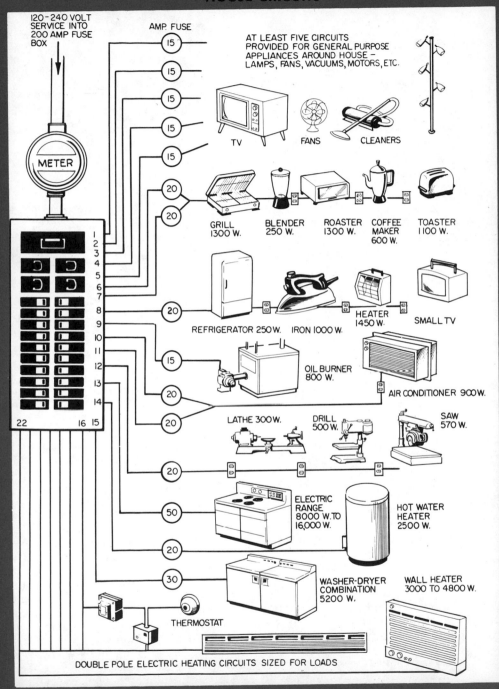

120-240 VOLT SERVICE INTO 200 AMP FUSE BOX

AMP. FUSE

15

15

15

15

15

AT LEAST FIVE CIRCUITS PROVIDED FOR GENERAL PURPOSE APPLIANCES AROUND HOUSE — LAMPS, FANS, VACUUMS, MOTORS, ETC.

TV

FANS

CLEANERS

METER

20

20

GRILL 1300 W.

BLENDER 250 W.

ROASTER 1300 W.

COFFEE MAKER 600 W.

TOASTER 1100 W.

1
2
3
4
5
6
7
8
9
10
11
12
13
14

22   16 15

20

REFRIGERATOR 250 W.   IRON 1000 W.

HEATER 1450 W.

SMALL TV

15

OIL BURNER 800 W.

AIR CONDITIONER 900 W.

20

20

LATHE 300 W.

DRILL 500 W.

SAW 570 W.

20

50

ELECTRIC RANGE 8000 W. TO 16,000 W.

HOT WATER HEATER 2500 W.

20

30

WASHER-DRYER COMBINATION 5200 W.

WALL HEATER 3000 TO 4800 W.

THERMOSTAT

DOUBLE POLE ELECTRIC HEATING CIRCUITS SIZED FOR LOADS

Modern circuit breaker service panel has main 100-ampere breaker, three 20-amp special appliance breakers, plus twelve circuit breakers for lights and appliances.

Fused service panel has main fused pull-out block (upper left), and pull-out block for range (upper right), plus six smaller fused circuits for lights and appliances.

across both hot wires is 240 volts. Depending on which wires are used, motors and appliances can use either voltage. If overhead, the wires are attached firmly to the house around insulators at least 10 feet above the ground. At that point "drip" loops of wire are connected to each wire and run into what is called an *entrance head*. Drip loops keep water from following wires into the entrance head.

From the entrance head wires run down the outside wall with a protective covering to the electric meter. Wires from the meter enter the house and run to a service panel. It is located nearby, to keep costly runs of heavy wires to a minimum. Since the entrance wiring has to carry every ampere of power that will be needed in the whole house, entrance wires must be heavy. Moreover, they are

so closely bunched that any heat formed is slow to dissipate.

HOUSE POWER

The service panel contains one or two large cartridge fuses, one for each hot wire. These may be rated at 30 amperes, 60, 100, 150 or even as much as 200 amperes and more. They indicate the total electric power available in your house. Sometimes, in modern panels, a pair of circuit breakers are used in place of fuses. A house with only 30-amp service, which usually employs two No. 8 wires, is considered inadequately wired. If your house has 30-amp service, you need to start at the pole, renewing everything up to and including the service panel.

Heavier 60-amp service is minimum. This uses three No. 6 wires, usually. It's not bad, unless you have (or want) an electric range, water heater and clothes dryer. It gives ample power for lighting and small portable appliances, but nothing extra for the big power-consuming appliances (see list).

Now considered best for homes with up to 3000 square feet of floor space is 100-ampere service. This makes use of three No. 3 wires (with RHW rubber insulation) or three No. 2 wires, most often. It provides service for lights and for small and major appliances that total up to 10,000 watts in power consumption.

All-electric homes with heating and air-conditioning require 150- and 200-amp service using 1/0 or 3/0 wire, respectively, with RHW rubber insulation.

HOUSE CIRCUITS

An adequately wired house provides circuits for all present and future needs. Each circuit takes off from the service panel. There the black wire of the circuit is fastened to an overcurrent device that protects the wires from being overloaded. This device is either a fuse or a circuit breaker. If the circuit is a 15-amp one, it uses No. 14 copper wire or No. 12 aluminum wire. A 20-amp circuit must use larger No. 12 copper or No. 10 aluminum wire. Aluminum wire is "relaxed" and easy to work. The larger size requirement is a drawback in making splices and in conduit runs where the maximum number of wires is limited according to wire size.

Only the "hot" side of any circuit is fused. The neutral side—the white wire—must never be fused. The white wire is connected to one of the terminals on the neutral strip inside the service panel. These make a direct unfused connection with the neutral entrance wire and with the ground connection.

The service panel itself and its grounding terminals are connected to a metal water pipe in the house. Ordinarily, this connection must be on the street side of a water meter, or the water meter must be bypassed with a grounding wire. This, so that a good ground will be intact, if the water meter is removed for repairs. In

HEAVY CURRENT APPLIANCES (AVERAGE POWER REQUIREMENTS)

Water heater — 2000 to 4500 watts
Range — 8,000 to 16,000 watts
Garbage disposer — 900 watts
Dishwasher (heating-type) — 1800 watts
Freezer, 12 cu. ft. — 600 watts
Electric clothes dryer — 4500 to 8700 watts
Automatic clothes washer — 650 to 900 watts
Fuel-fired heating plant — 100 to 800 watts
Central air conditioning — 5000 watts
Water pump — 300 to 700 watts
Built-in room heater — 1600 watts

MAXIMUM LENGTH OF CIRCUIT (FEET)

WATTS	WIRE SIZE			
	No. 14	No. 12	No. 10	No. 8
500	100	200	300	400
1000	70	100	175	300
1800*	40	70	100	150
2400**		50	80	125

*15-ampere circuit maximum
**20-ampere circuit maximum

ALLOWABLE CURRENT-CARRYING CAPACITY OF INSULATED CONDUCTORS (LOWEST CURRENT-CARRYING INSULATION TYPES)

WIRE SIZE	AMPERES	
	Copper	Aluminum
No. 14	15	- -
No. 12	20	15
No. 10	30	25
No. 8	40	30
No. 6	55	40
No. 4	70	55
No. 3	80	65
No. 2	95	75
No. 1	110	85
No. 0	125	100
No. 2/0	145	115
No. 3/0	165	130

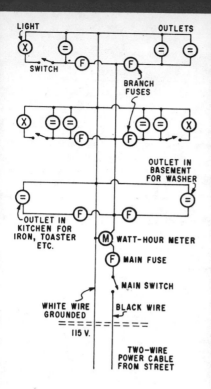

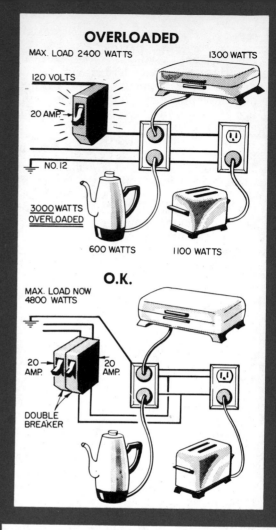

Top diagram shows basic hookup of two-wire power distribution generally found in older residences. Bottom figure shows basic three-wire system, which makes both 115 and 230 volts available for use in home.

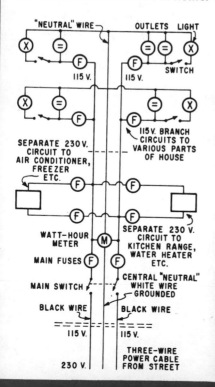

houses without underground piping the ground connection is made to a long copper rod or galvanized pipe driven into the ground. Bare grounding wires or the metal conduit in every run throughout house circuits carry ground continuity to every outlet. Never ground to a gas pipe or to a plumbing system with a plastic entrance main. The white wire is a *neutral*, not a ground. Only in 3-wire 240-volt circuits is it used as a grounding wire. Good grounding protects house wiring against lightning and shocks caused by barbed wires in circuit or appliances.

HOLDS MAIN FUSES

A main disconnect inside the service

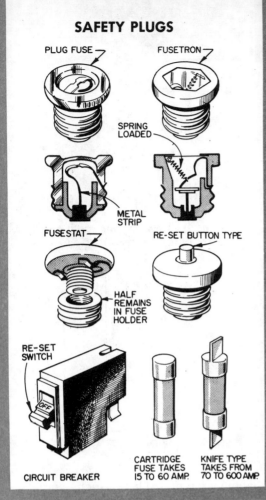

SAFETY PLUGS

PLUG FUSE

FUSETRON

SPRING
LOADED

METAL
STRIP

FUSESTAT

RE-SET BUTTON TYPE

HALF
REMAINS
IN FUSE
HOLDER

RE-SET
SWITCH

CIRCUIT BREAKER

CARTRIDGE
FUSE TAKES
15 TO 60 AMP.

KNIFE TYPE
TAKES FROM
70 TO 600 AMP.

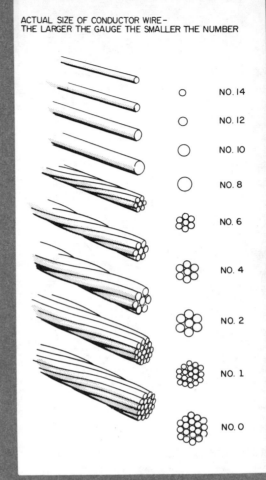

ACTUAL SIZE OF CONDUCTOR WIRE –
THE LARGER THE GAUGE THE SMALLER THE NUMBER

NO. 14

NO. 12

NO. 10

NO. 8

NO. 6

NO. 4

NO. 2

NO. 1

NO. 0

panel holds the main fuses. Pulling this out cuts off all power to the house. If the main protection uses circuit breakers, they can be turned off to cut power to the house.

Fuses or breakers are wired integrally with the service panel, to divide equally both "hot" sides of the circuit.

House circuits are classed as general purpose, appliance or special purpose.

General purpose circuits serve house lights and receptacles for small appliances. Modern ones are 20-amp. One 20-ampere general purpose circuit is recommended for each 500 square feet of floorspace. One 15-amp general purpose circuit should serve only 375 square feet. For instance, a 2000-square-foot house would need at least four general purpose 20-amp circuits. This is minimum. Five such circuits would be better. You can put as many outlets as you want on a circuit, but don't exceed the 500/375 square feet of floorspace served. Also don't wire the circuit to serve more appliances than its capacity will handle. Ordinarily, if you don't exceed the floorspace maximum, the circuit should not be overloaded. A circuit serving a workshop would be an exception. Big motors use lots of amps.

KITCHEN CIRCUITS

The National Code requires at least two 20-amp grounded-type circuits for kitchen, laundry and dining room appliances. These must be separate from any

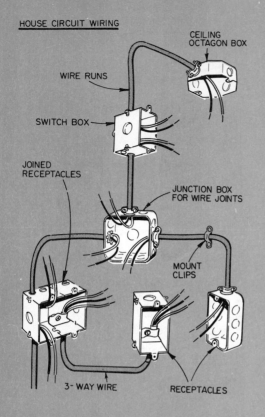

HOUSE CIRCUIT WIRING

WIRE RUNS

CEILING OCTAGON BOX

SWITCH BOX

JOINED RECEPTACLES

JUNCTION BOX FOR WIRE JOINTS

MOUNT CLIPS

3-WAY WIRE

RECEPTACLES

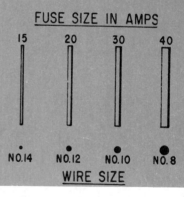

All circuits lead away from service panel, here in conduit, to various parts of house.

FUSE SIZE IN AMPS

15	20	30	40
NO.14	NO.12	NO.10	NO.8

WIRE SIZE

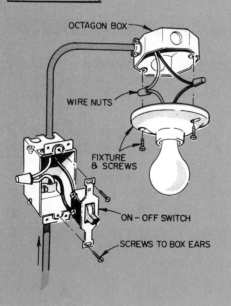

LIGHT CIRCUIT WIRING

OCTAGON BOX

WIRE NUTS

FIXTURE & SCREWS

ON – OFF SWITCH

SCREWS TO BOX EARS

lighting circuit. Three such circuits would be better.

General purpose circuits should include enough convenience receptacles — those not allocated for any special appliance — so there is one within every 12 feet of running wall space. This gives flexibility to furniture arrangement and does away with the need for many extension cords. In the kitchen, you need receptacles every 4 feet along counter space for plugging in small appliances. You also need outdoor, basement workshop and garage outlets to make house wiring fully useful.

Special purpose circuits serve heavy current-using appliances such as a range, dishwasher, waste disposal, furnace, well pump, electric clothes dryer and water heater. Some of these are 240-volt circuits wired with three-conductor cable

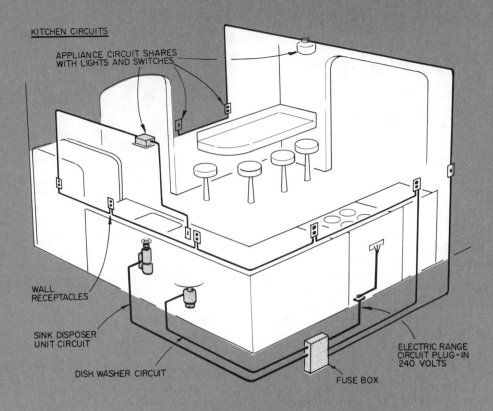

KITCHEN CIRCUITS

APPLIANCE CIRCUIT SHARES
WITH LIGHTS AND SWITCHES

WALL
RECEPTACLES

SINK DISPOSER
UNIT CIRCUIT

DISH WASHER CIRCUIT

FUSE BOX

ELECTRIC RANGE
CIRCUIT PLUG-IN
240 VOLTS

containing the black "hot" wire, the white neutral wire and another "hot" wire coded red. The circuit may be wired to a special 240-volt appliance receptacle or directly to the box on the appliance or motor. Any appliance or motor which does not plug in must have some other means of quick disconnect. This usually means that a switch box must be provided within sight of the appliance.

TOOLS GO SLUGGISH

Voltage drop can be a problem in long runs to circuits. For instance, a house that is 70 feet long needs a larger size wire for a run from the service panel at one end to the attic at the other. Voltage drop makes tools and appliances sluggish and slow to do what they're supposed to.

Lights dim when heavy-draw appliances are used. See the accompanying chart.

Some houses also contain sub-panels, branches that draw power from power takeoff lugs on the fused side of the main service panel. These sub-panels contain fuses or circuit breakers of their own. Separate house circuits take off from the sub-panels to serve the house, garage or out buildings. In long houses the sub-panel may be used to avoid voltage drop in overly long circuits. Voltage drop is an electrical bad actor. Good wiring is planned to avoid it.

A typical adequately wired house may contain five general purpose circuits, three kitchen-laundry-dining room appliance circuits and 10 special purpose circuits. This is a tremendous difference from the two-circuit houses some of us grew up in.

WHAT TO DO WHEN A FUSE BLOWS

This safety device is warning you

that your lines are overloaded

Main fuses are cartridge type. They fit between clips in back of fuse pullout block. Two are needed for 240-volt, 3-wire service.

A fuse or circuit breaker is a safety device. When one blows, it is trying to tell you that something is wrong. At the same time it is protecting your home from fire. Joule's Law is working against you when too much current tries to flow through a wire too small and too long to carry it. Heat is produced, and the heat increases as the square of current flows. Two times the current equals four times the heat; four times the current, 16 times the heat. Homeowners who keep adding more electrical gadgets to already-overloaded circuits would be in real trouble if it were not for the protection of house fuses. Without their limiting the electrical flow to what each circuit can stand, fire would be inevitable. So be grateful when a fuse does blow. It may have saved you from big trouble.

WHY THEY BLOW

Fuses blow and breakers trip chiefly for the following reasons: overloaded circuit, bare wires touching, grounded wires in house or appliance wiring, or a large motor starting up.

A fuse that has been blown by a short-circuit has its mica window blackened by the vaporizing element. A fuse blown slowly by overloading has a clean window. Its filament merely melts at the thinnest spot.

Too many appliances drawing too much juice at one time is the biggest cause of fuse blowing. If new fuses work

for hours, days or weeks and then blow again, that's a sign. What you need is a circuit survey. Unscrew the affected fuse, or switch off the one breaker. Then run around the house with a test light or plug-in lamp turned on and test the receptacles. List those outlets served by that fuse. They'll be dead. Test the room lights, too. Then see whether you can move appliance plugs to throw part of the load onto other circuits. Another way out is to juggle appliance use, limiting the load to what the circuit can take.

If the cost of buying new fuses has you down, forget it. Get a pushbutton reset fuse. Just push the button on a blown fuse and it's ready to serve again.

Whatever you do, don't use a larger fuse than the wire in the circuit calls for —No. 14 wire, 15-amp.; No. 12 wire, 20-amp. Don't bypass fuses, either, by putting something metal behind them.

BARE WIRES

Short-circuited wires make every new fuse you install blow immediately. Finding the short-circuit is the problem. First unplug everything and turn off all lights, to try to eliminate appliances and light circuits as the bad spot. Then remove outlet cover plates and receptacles. Look for bare wires or a wire end grounded to an outlet box. If the short-circuit is inside a cable—unlikely—you'll have to take apart every splice in the circuit until you isolate the affected cable. A new cable will have to be run in place of the old

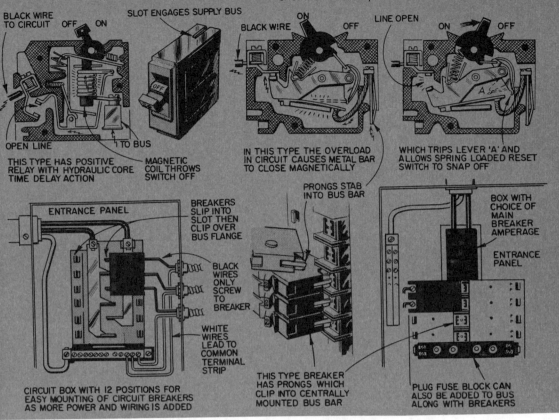

BEFORE AND AFTER VIEWS OF ACTION IN BREAKER
SHOWING POWER ON, THEN RESULTS OF OVERLOADING

BLACK WIRE
TO CIRCUIT   OFF   ON

SLOT ENGAGES SUPPLY BUS

BLACK WIRE   OFF   LINE OPEN

ON   OFF

OPEN LINE   TO BUS

THIS TYPE HAS POSITIVE
RELAY WITH HYDRAULIC CORE
TIME DELAY ACTION

MAGNETIC
COIL THROWS
SWITCH OFF

IN THIS TYPE THE OVERLOAD
IN CIRCUIT CAUSES METAL BAR
TO CLOSE MAGNETICALLY

WHICH TRIPS LEVER 'A' AND
ALLOWS SPRING LOADED RESET
SWITCH TO SNAP OFF

PRONGS STAB
INTO BUS BAR

BOX WITH
CHOICE OF
MAIN
BREAKER
AMPERAGE

ENTRANCE PANEL

BREAKERS
SLIP INTO
SLOT THEN
CLIP OVER
BUS FLANGE

ENTRANCE
PANEL

BLACK
WIRES
ONLY
SCREW
TO
BREAKER

WHITE
WIRES
LEAD TO
COMMON
TERMINAL
STRIP

CIRCUIT BOX WITH 12 POSITIONS FOR
EASY MOUNTING OF CIRCUIT BREAKERS
AS MORE POWER AND WIRING IS ADDED

THIS TYPE BREAKER
HAS PRONGS WHICH
CLIP INTO CENTRALLY
MOUNTED BUS BAR

PLUG FUSE BLOCK CAN
ALSO BE ADDED TO BUS
ALONG WITH BREAKERS

one to correct the problem.

When a wire inside a grounded appliance contacts the appliance body the fuse will blow. Fix the appliance immediately.

MOTOR BLOWS FUSE

When starting, electric motors draw two or three times their normal operating current. This can easily overload a circuit if other appliances are going at the same time. The simplest solution is to install time-delay fuses. These fuses are often called *Fustats* or *Fusetrons*, both trade names. *Fustats* are tamper-free; that is, they fit into a special socket. Once the socket is screwed into a fuse opening it won't come out. The only *Fustats* that will work in that opening are those of the right size or smaller. Larger ones won't fit. A *Fusetron* has a screwbase the same as a normal fuse plug. Both will pass a temporary surge of current over the maximum intended. If a steady overcurrent tries to sneak by, it can do so only momentarily. Then the time-delay feature springs into action and the fuse blows. The greater the overcurrent, the quicker it blows the fuse. Time-delay fuses are excellent for all house wiring circuits.

Circuit breakers have a built-in time-delay feature. The whole idea is to let the circuit take a momentary overcurrent — as long as it is momentary.

A time-delay fuse blown by a short has a dirty window. Its spring and filament are attached at the base. The same fuse blown by a steady overload has a clean window and an intact filament. The spring lets go at the fuse base.

Always have a few extra fuses handy. None should be larger than the capacity of your house circuits.

41

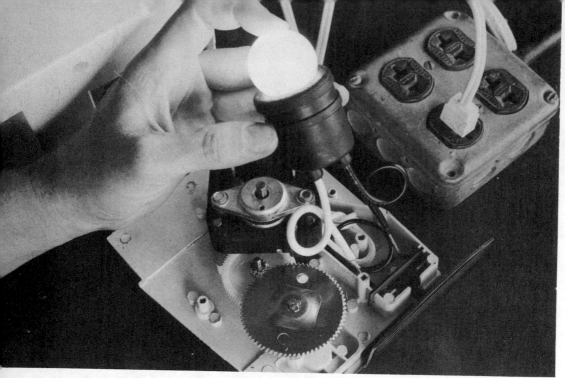

When you have a suspicious appliance cord and plug, the basic test to check its efficiency is to put the probes of a test light across the terminals of the appliance when plugged in.

GROUND RULES OF APPLIANCE REPAIR

Repairs can be simple — if you have a VO meter and enjoy the puzzle

Treat your appliances right and they usually will last many years without servicing. But with all the appliances used in homes today the need for service is bound to come up. Mostly it's a simple repair. You can do it yourself if you know what to look for — and how to look.

Before you dive into any appliance repair ask yourself whether you *should* do it yourself. Many small appliances are guaranteed for one year from the date of purchase. If something goes wrong, you have only to take the appliance back where you got it and get another one free. Major appliances also have guarantees. You can void a guarantee by working on the appliance yourself.

Furthermore, don't try to repair appliances unless you know what you're doing and enjoy it. Appliance repair is like working a puzzle or taking apart a clock to see what makes it tick. Often fixing an appliance is easier than solving a puzzle. More often the biggest problem is getting the appliance apart. For good looks some manufacturers hide the fastenings that hold the body of the appliance together. The fasteners are rarely obvious. Sometimes, once you find them, they're downright discouraging. Some appliances have rivets that must be filed down before the body can be taken apart.

DOES IT NEED TAKE-APART?

Do all the testing you can without taking the dern thing apart. Make sure it needs take-apart before you try. Often there is merely an open wire at the plug. Cut the cord, install a new plug, and it works again. Even before you do that, check the receptacle to make sure it has power. Perhaps a fuse is blown.

Other problems that appliances develop are not electrical, but mechanical. The troubleshooting procedures for popular appliances given in another chapter stress electrical troubles, their causes and cures.

Never work on an appliance that is plugged in. You can make certain electrical tests with the plug in, but unplug it again right away. If you plug in a disassembled appliance, remember that the exposed leads, heating elements and other parts are live wires. Treat them that way — always.

VO METER

In line with making it fun to fix home appliances is the VO meter. Great accuracy of meters is not needed in appliance work, so you needn't spend a great deal for a meter. Better to have a low-cost one than do without.

The VO meter is useful for testing AC and DC voltages as well as circuit resistances. If you do much appliance or motor repair, you'll find a VO meter indispensable. It can tell you lots about the appliance without your ever disassembling it.

A VO meter usually has a selector switch to let it be adjusted for measuring different amounts of volts and ohms. For instance, a good meter has voltage settings for measuring as little as 1½ volts and testing voltages to 1½, 5, 15, 50, 150, 500 and sometimes more. It has

SAMPLE OHM READINGS	
APPLIANCE	OHMS
Clock	600 to 1200
Toaster (two-slice)	12 to 18
Waffle iron	8 to 10
Deep fat fryer	10
Rotisserie	9
Coffee maker	24
Hand iron	12 to 13
Heating pad	300
Electric blanket (double)	100
Vacuum cleaner	1 to 2
Table fan	20 to 30
Electric knife	40
Electric can opener	8
Shaver	140
Hair dryer	25
¼-inch drill	10 to 20
½-inch drill	4 to 9
Belt sander	3 to 9
Portable circular saw, 7-inch	4
1/20-H.P. split-phase motor	7
¼-H.P. split-phase motor	1 to 4
⅓-H.P. split-phase motor	0.8
⅓-H.P. capacitor motor	1.5
½-H.P. capacitor motor	0.6 to 1.2
¾-H.P. capacitor saw motor	1

Getting an appliance apart can be the biggest problem in fixing it. Look for hidden screws, rivets and other holding devices.

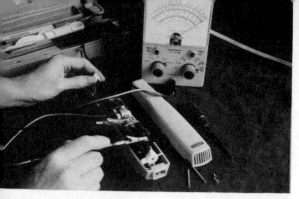

There's nothing like VO meter for making all sorts of electrical checks on appliance circuits. Get one if you make many repairs.

VO meter should have range of voltages and resistances. The ranges are made available by a selector switch set for each test.

ohm scales for measuring from 0 to infinite ohms. Each higher ohm class is 10 times the one below it. Where the resistance is high, the meter can be set for the highest ohm scale. Then it can even measure the resistance through your body as you hold the test prods in your hands. Where the resistance is very low, it can be set on the lowest resistance scale. Then the meter can measure resistance through the windings of an electric motor or through the corroded contacts of a switch.

You can use the voltage scale for checking batteries, house voltages, voltage leaks from faulty appliances, voltage drop across the contacts of a switch and house voltage drop when a heavy motor starts up.

SETTING THE SCALE

When testing a known voltage, always set the scale for the next higher voltage. For instance, to make a voltage test on a 6-volt lantern battery, set the volt selector at 15 volts. The needle scale will come not quite half-way to the 6-volt mark on the 15-volt scale. If you were to set the voltage selector at 5 volts, and connect it to 110 volts, the needle would jump off the scale. This is not good for the instrument and would probably finish it for good. Think before you make each test.

When testing an unknown voltage, always start with the selector in the highest voltage position and work down one notch at a time until you get a good reading. Follow the specific instructions with the VO meter you are using.

Never take an ohm reading on a "hot" circuit. The VO meter had its own battery that provides power for ohm readings.

On the other hand, voltage readings must be taken on an energized circuit.

Use VO meter to check for low voltage at appliance terminals with unit plugged in and selector set for AC volt readings over 1000 volts. Caution: water-holding appliances can be damaged by plugging in when empty.

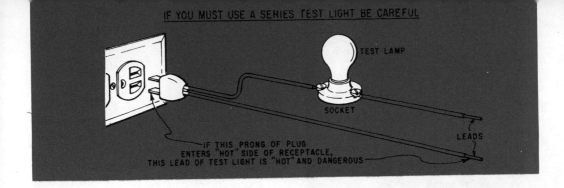

TEST LAMP

SOCKET

LEADS

IF THIS PRONG OF PLUG
ENTERS "HOT" SIDE OF RECEPTACLE,
THIS LEAD OF TEST LIGHT IS "HOT" AND DANGEROUS

Otherwise, there would be no voltage to measure.

TEST LIGHT

If you must do without a VO meter, make or buy a test light. The prods can be touched across any two wires to tell if there is voltage between them. If the lamp lights, there is. If it doesn't, there is little if any voltage.

A test light can be used to test receptacles to see if power is available in them. You can use it to test across the terminals of an appliance while it is plugged in. This checks out the cord. You can test between the closed switch or thermostat and the unswitched line at the terminal to see that they are making good electrical contact. If the lamp lights, they probably are. By using a larger wattage test lamp you can test a switch under a heavier load. Bulb size should be matched to the appliance's normal load for the best test of a switch.

One kind of home-made test light, called the series test light, has been widely illustrated in books on electrical repair. It can be dangerous. If you have one be careful with it. Two wires come out from a plug. One lead has a light wired into it. When the leads are touched, the lamp lights. Depending on which way the plug faces when you plug it in, the untapped lead can be a "hot" wire carrying the full 120 volts and 15 amps of the house circuit with no light between to offer resistance. When you touch it to an appliance, the whole appliance body becomes "live." It's best to let the professionals use this kind of light.

You can buy another kind of tester

Same test is made without a VO meter by using test light across appliance terminals. Brightness of light indicates the voltage.

The continuity test is basic to all appliance repairs. Set a VO meter for high ohms and hook its probes across appliance plug. The reading should drop from infinite ohms to zero ohms when the switch is turned on.

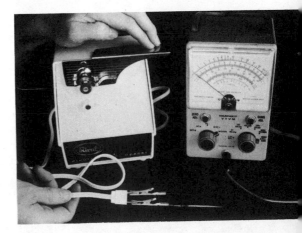

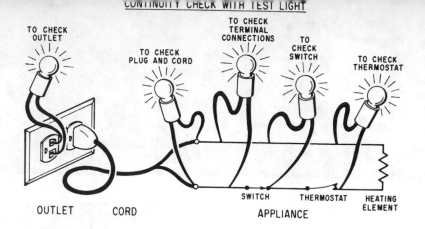

With a test light the continuity test is made with the particular appliance plugged in and the light then placed across the leads to the motor or the heating element.

There should be no continuity between appliance's electrical leads and body. If meter reading falls much from infinity on high-ohm scale, look inside for a grounded wire.

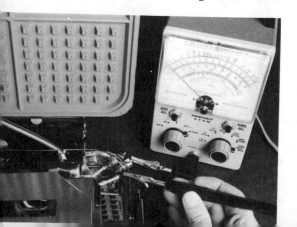

that has some uses a homemade test light can't match. It's a neon tester. Two test prods are wired to a neon lamp. The lamp glows under the slightest voltage. While it won't load a circuit being tested, it will test across the terminals of a switch or thermostat for voltage drop through it. If with the contacts closed, the neon tube glows, there is voltage drop. Perhaps the contacts need cleaning.

Low-voltage circuit testers come in flashlight form with test probes. You could make one easily enough by soldering a wire to the bulb's center terminal and another to the case.

BASIC TESTS

Familiarize yourself with three basic electrical tests and you'll be able to handle most electrical troubleshooting. These are the *continuity test,* the *resistance test* and the *voltage drop test.* Perhaps the most useful test is for circuit continuity. If electricity will flow through a circuit, it has a continuous path, or continuity.

By setting a VO meter for ohm-testing, the prods are energized with a slight voltage. When you touch them to anything that will carry electricity, the current flows from one test prod through the circuit and back to the other prod. The ohm meter needle moves when the prods are connected to a circuit with continuity. The meter measures the rate of electrical flow and interprets the result as ohms.

If the current flows abundantly, the

With a sensitive VO meter you can even measure your body's resistance to electricity. Set the scale on high ohms, then watch the needle fall as you grasp the test probes.

Bad ground could be caused by a heating element wire kocked from its insulator in a shipping accident. Check all new appliances for bad grounds before using them.

meter reads low ohms (low resistance). If the current flows only meagerly, the meter reads high ohms (high resistance). Low ohm readings of less then 1 ohm and high ohm readings to infinity are possible with a good ohm meter. If there is current flow, which is shown by readings of less then infinity on the high ohms scale, the circuit has continuity. If there is no current flow, the circuit is open. Never test a "live" circuit for ohms. Take the plug out.

Your test light will make continuity checks on "live" circuits without telling you much about resistance. If the lamp lights, there is continuity. If the lamp won't light, the circuit is open (see illustrations).

The continuity test is used to look for loose connections, switches that won't carry current, open thermostats, broken wires, and burned-out lamps.

Testing ground continuity of an appliance with a sensitive neon test light is done with unit plugged in and operating. Touch probes from appliance body to a good ground such as metal sink. Light shouldn't glow.

OPEN CIRCUITS

Sometimes an open circuit is desirable. For example, when you throw a switch to *off*, the switch must create an open circuit to stop the flow of electricity and shut off the appliance. You also want an open circuit between the separate windings of an electric motor. If they should become interconnected, the motor would not run right. In testing for an open circuit the VO meter needle should show infinite ohms on the high-ohm scale or the test lamp should not light.

Most appliances should be grounded to the round prong of a grounding plug. There should be less than half an ohm resistance between the body of the appliance and the plug. Set the VO meter on the low-ohm scale.

Grounding check can be made with 100-watt or larger bulb in a test light. Plug appliance in and plug one probe of light into the hot side of an extension cord. Touch other probe to appliance. Light should burn brightly, indicating good circuit to ground.

Check your receptacles for ground with VO meter by taking a voltage reading across the small hot opening and the round ground opening. It's easy to do if you insert a plug part way and tap its hot prong. Reading should show house voltage — 115 volts.

A variation of the continuity test is the ground continuity test. An appliance can be dangerous if any of the internal wiring is touching the body of the appliance. When a motor winding is grounded to the frame or to the shaft, the motor is in trouble; the user may be, too. In these instances there should be no continuity between the circuit and the body of the motor or appliance.

To test for this kind of ground continuity the VO meter prods are touched across one of the flat plug prongs and the body of the appliance. The selector should be on the highest ohm setting. The appliance should be unplugged but its switch should be on. The meter needle should barely move from the infinity position. Very slight movement is permissible. This indicates a teeny current leakage across insulators and an air gap. It should, however, be many times less than the needle moved when you hold the prods in opposite hands. An indication of continuity from the "live" circuit to the appliance body is bad. Something must be fixed before you use the appliance. Take it apart and find the bad ground.

GROUND TEST

You can't make a reliable ground test with a test light, though it will show up a strong ground. The ground continuity test is made with a test light while the appliance is plugged in. Touch one prod to the appliance body, the other to a water pipe or other good ground. If the lamp even glows, fix the bad ground immediately. You're looking at a dangerous appliance.

Since the amount of current it takes to kill wouldn't light a Christmas tree lamp, also make the test with a volt meter set on low scale and connected as described for the test light.

After you finish repairing any appliance, make a continuity check for a bad ground. In fact, as soon as you get your VO meter learn how to use it to make a bad ground check on all your appliances. Do the same with every new appliance before using it. During shipping an insulator can get broken or a terminal pulled loose. Without a ground test, you may not know if the item is unsafe until someone gets shocked. Sometimes the leakage is slight, barely more than a slight tingle when you rub lightly across the metal body. That's too much. A tingle today can be lethal tomorrow. Fix it. Also, don't hold the appliance while you plug it in if you're grounded.

A THIRD CIRCUIT

Electric drills, saws and many other

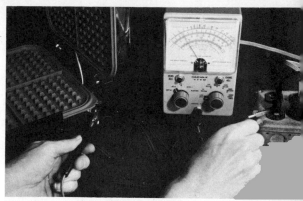

Measure the voltage drop across a suspected circuit — in this case the thermostat of a briefly plugged-in coffee maker. Always set the meter on low volts. The voltage drop reading should be a few volts or less.

To measure the voltage drop of a power cord, take a low-volts reading from one end of one wire to the other while the appliance is operating. The voltage drop reading should always be a few volts or less.

small household appliances these days are either double-insulated or grounded. This sort of grounding is different. It isn't the "live" circuit that is grounded to the appliance body, but a third green-wired grounding circuit. The grounding wire is attached to the appliance at one end and wired to the longest prong of a three-prong plug at the other. When plugged into a grounded three-hole outlet, the third wire effectively grounds the body of the appliance to prevent accidental shock while using it.

You can tell the good guys from the bad guys with your VO meter or test light. Using a VO meter, touch one lead to the body of the appliance and the other to the grounding prong of the three-prong plug. There should be complete continuity. The ohm scale should be on its lowest ohm setting and the needle should flick to *0 ohms*. This signifies that there is a complete grounded circuit from the tool to the plug's prong.

The same test can be made with a test light on the plugged-in appliance. The appliance should rest on a nonconductive surface. Put one prod of the light in the "hot" side of a receptacle. This is the one with the shortest hole. Touch the other prod to the body of the appliance. The lamp should light brightly.

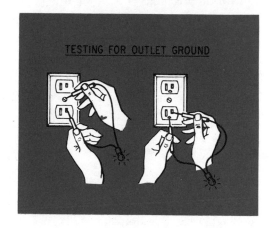

TESTING FOR OUTLET GROUND

BOTH TESTS DESIRABLE

Both the ohm test and the test light check are desirable. The test light (depending on its size) proves the ability of the ground circuit to carry current. Ideally the ground should have enough capacity to blow a fuse. Have serious doubts about any ground system that won't light a 100-watt lamp to full brilliance.

If there is not good ground continuity, part of the grounded circuit is open. The trouble may be in the appliance or in your house wiring. Find it and fix it.

You can check the house circuit ground by taking a voltage reading with your VO meter. Set the volt selector

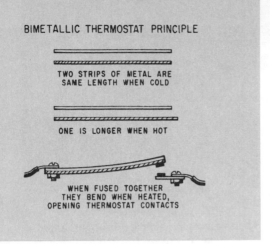

BIMETALLIC THERMOSTAT PRINCIPLE

TWO STRIPS OF METAL ARE
SAME LENGTH WHEN COLD

ONE IS LONGER WHEN HOT

WHEN FUSED TOGETHER
THEY BEND WHEN HEATED,
OPENING THERMOSTAT CONTACTS

Neon test light is sensitive enough to record minute voltage drops across switches when appliance is plugged in and the switch closed. The indicator never should glow.

higher than 120 volts. Touch the prods to the "hot" hole of the receptacle and the grounding hole. You should get the same voltage reading as when the prods are touched across the "hot" and neutral holes. (The neutral is the wider of the two parallel holes). If you don't, either the outlet is not grounded or the black and white leads to it are reversed. Take it out and investigate further with a test light and VO meter.

You can have fun going around to all your receptacles and testing them this way.

HOW TO TEST

The same check can be made with the test light. It's a better check because it proves at least some current-carrying ability, if a 100-watt lamp is used. Plug the test probes in across the "hot" hole and the grounding hole. The lamp should light with full brilliance. No light or a weak light is a tipoff to trouble.

Your VO meter also is useful for making voltage drop readings. These can be helpful in ferreting out a faulty switch or thermostat. With the body off and the appliance plugged in and operating at full load, carefully take a voltage reading across the two terminals of the switch or thermostat contact points. There should not be more than a few volts potential. If the potential is, say, 10 volts across the switch, that means it is stealing 10 volts of electrical pressure from your

appliance. Contact cleaning or switch replacement is the cure.

You can likewise test the voltage drop from one end of a power cord to the other. With the appliance under load, test across one plug prong to the same wire at the other end of the power cord. The plug must not be all the way in so the prong is accessible. The appliance body must be partly disassembled to expose the cord end.

THERMOSTATS

Many household appliances use tiny thermostats to switch resistance heating coils on and off and maintain the desired temperature. Irons, toasters, coffee makers, waffle irons and electric cooking utensils all use thermostats. All are basically the same. Two metal contact points make and break the electrical flow. The contacts are often made of silver. One of the contacts is mounted on a bimetallic metal arm. This has two metals fused into one piece. When heated, one of the metals expands much more than the other, making the combination bend. The hotter the arm gets, the more it bends.

In operation, the bimetallic arm bends backward until its contact no longer touches the other contact. The power to the heating element is thus shut off. The appliance cools until the arm straightens out enough for the contacts to touch again. The circuit is closed again, and re-

Adjustable thermostats have one arm that is moved in and out when dial is turned. This changes distance that the bimetallic arm must move to open or close the circuit.

For resistance test, appliance is unplugged and switched on. Take reading across plug's flat prongs. Infinite resistance means open circuit. No resistance means short-circuit.

heating begins. The cycle is repeated over and over. Temperatures may vary only 5 to 10 degrees during an *off-on* cycle.

One contact is adjustable; that is, it can be moved in or out by turning the temperature dial. For higher temperature settings it closes the gap with the other contact making the bimetallic arm bend more to shut off the current. For lower temperature settings, it opens the gap.

USE OF MAGNET

Sometimes one of the contacts is backed with a small magnet to make it cling tightly until the bimetallic force is enough to pull it loose. This makes the contact action rapid and positive. Arcing is reduced and the contacts last longer.

In time the contacts may get corroded or burned. Then they need cleaning or the thermostat needs replacing. You can buy a thermostat from an appliance parts dealer. You'll have to show him the old thermostat or give the make, model and size of your appliance.

OHM TESTING

A VO meter can help you determine whether an appliance has the proper resistance. If a switch or thermostat is making poor contact, the resistance will be too high. So will it be if one of two heating elements is electrically open. An internal short-circuit will make the resistance too low.

An ohm test can be made in a minute

without taking the appliance apart. Set the ohm selector on the lowest range. Turn the appliance switch to *on* and connect the prods across the flat prongs of the plug. If the reading is very high, wiggle the thermostat and flick the switch to see if it drops. Suppose the reading on an electric iron comes to 13 ohms. You can tell if that is good or bad by converting it to the amperes the appliance will draw by dividing the ohm reading into the voltage, 115 (115÷13=8.8 amps). Thus, the appliance should draw 8.8 amps when plugged in. If the iron nameplate gives watts instead of amps, you can convert this easily to amps by dividing by the voltage (1000 watts÷115 volts =8.7 amps).

The less the wattage draw of an appliance, the greater the resistance.

Using the simplified formula: watts= 13,225÷ohms, you can check out any heating appliance with an ohm meter, if you know its wattage. The results cannot be exact, because every heating element increases in resistance when it gets hot. You can only check the cold resistance. Still, it's a way to check out an appliance without much trouble.

The method won't work on electric motors. Their initial resistance is far lower than their power draw would indicate. The reason is that when it is running, the motor's windings create backvoltage. Back-voltage holds current flow back, making it much less than the ohm reading would indicate.

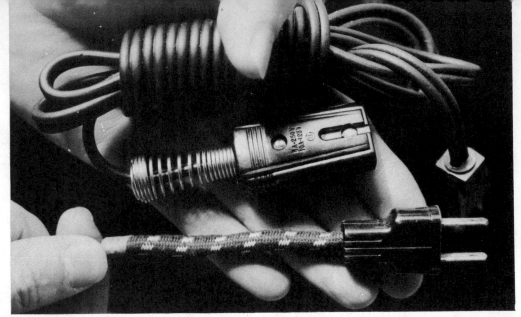

Two types of heater cord, rubber (top) and asbestos-insulated (bottom). Most modern heating appliances use rubber cord. It is lighter, tougher and much more flexible.

CORD KINKS

Familiarize yourself with specialized cord sets, types and safety features

Cords are a regular part of your electrical living. You use them for reaching outlets that aren't close enough to plug appliances into directly. Don't be hamstrung by cords. You'll find one for every need.

A cord, a plug and a length of cable — usually at least six feet long — with a plug on one end and a tap on the other — is called a *cord set*. Cord sets are designed to provide a quick, easy disconnect from whatever appliance they are plugged to. Often the plugs and taps are molded integrally with the cord.

Another kind of cord is the power supply cord. One of these comes attached to every appliance you buy. When one wears out or deteriorates, it must be replaced. Here is some information on choosing a replacement. How to install it is covered in another chapter.

FLEXIBLE CORDS

Cords are either round, jacketed or flat. They're designed to be flexible. Jacketed cords have stranded copper conductors, two or three; thermoplastic insulation, usually; fillers, usually jute; a separator for the conductors; and a thermoplastic jacket.

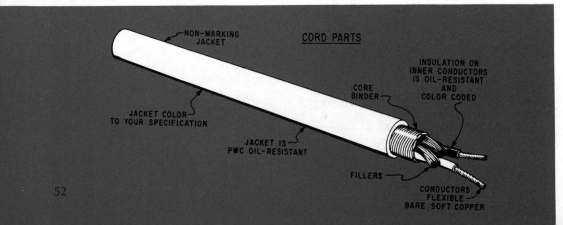

CORD PARTS

NON-MARKING JACKET

INSULATION ON INNER CONDUCTORS IS OIL-RESISTANT AND COLOR CODED

CORE BINDER

JACKET COLOR TO YOUR SPECIFICATION

JACKET IS PWC OIL-RESISTANT

FILLERS

CONDUCTORS FLEXIBLE BARE SOFT COPPER

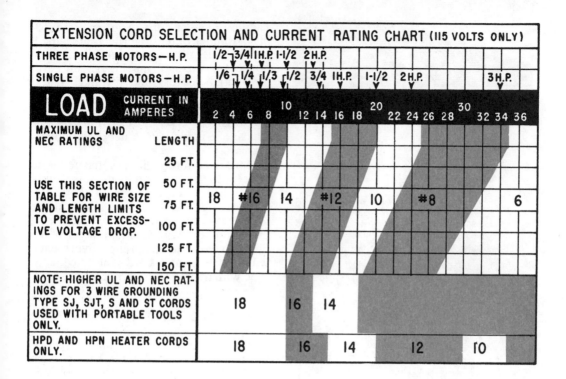

EXTENSION CORD SELECTION AND CURRENT RATING CHART (115 VOLTS ONLY)

Flat cords offer a low-cost material for use where the service is not severe enough to call for a jacketed cord. Typical uses are lamps, fans, blenders and phonographs, and as light-duty extension cords. Two- or three-stranded copper conductors are covered with thermoplastic insulation.

For additional properties—abrasion resistance, oil resistance, etc.—cords with rubber, neoprene and tougher plastic coverings are available.

Sizes of cords range from No. 18 to No. 10 and even larger. National Electric Code ratings for these cords are: No. 18 – 7 amps; No. 16 – 10 amps; No. 14 – 15 amps; No. 12 – 20 amps; and No. 10 – 25 amps.

Wiring that is not used for house circuits is called cord. The most familiar is Underwriters Type SP or SPT. Nicknamed "zip" cord, it's the two-wire material that most small appliances are fitted with. The two halves can be zipped apart when making connections. Most common size is No. 18, but heavier gauges are available. A three-wire version also is made. Type SP has rubber covering. Type SPT has plastic insulation. The data is sometimes on the cord.

Other times you'll have to look at the reel it comes from. Various colors are available, and the cord is low in cost. Use it for low-current-draw appliances such as lamps and radios where the load is not high enough to heat the wire. Long wires should be avoided to prevent a voltage drop due to increased resistance. "Zip" cord should not be subjected to wear, like a vacuum cleaner cord takes, or oil as might be received by a garage droplight cord.

BETTER-QUALITY CORDS

A step-up in quality (and cost) is Type S cord, which is round and insulated with rubber. Type ST is the same but is plastic insulated. Each conductor is insulated, too. Types S and ST are for use where the cord will receive abrasion, such as a

Damaged cord should be replaced immediately. Do not tape it up and keep on using it.

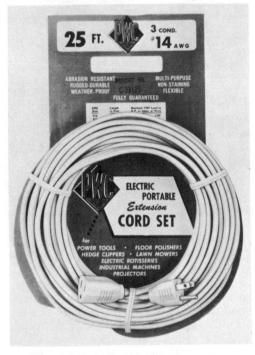

With portable power tools, like an electric drill, you need a 3-wire extension cord set.

With a 3-wire cord you can plug tools into grounding tap and safely ground tool body.

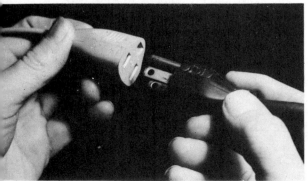

vacuum cleaner cord. Another type, SJ, has a thinner outer covering than Type S and is generally more useful around the house for washing machines, refrigerators, small motors and the like. The *J* means *junior.* Oil-resistant cord of this kind is designated Type SO-EZC for Type S and SJO-EZC for Type SJ. These are made with a neoprene covering.

Cord used for appliances that generate heat, such as irons and heaters, is simply called heater cord. Type HPD is the Underwriter's designation. The outside of HPD heater cord is a woven covering of cotton or rayon. Inside, a layer of asbestos wool and neoprene covers each wire. HPN heater cord is a "zip" cord type with neoprene covering.

SAME TYPE, LENGTH

Many other cords are highly specialized. See your dealer for the unusual. When replacing an appliance cord, be sure to get the same type of cord that originally came with the appliance. You should stick to the same length, too. This avoids having too much resistance from an overly long appliance cord. Don't overload a cord by using one that's too small for the job.

Extension cords should be heavy enough to handle the load and the distance without excessive voltage drop. It can be a big problem with extension cords. See the table and follow its recommendations.

A ¼-inch electric drill draws about 2½ amps; ½-inch, 3½ amps. A saber saw takes 2½ amps. A 7-inch portable power saw requires some 8 amps. Figure to 10 amps for a belt sander, according to size. An orbital sander takes about 3½ amps. Floor polisher, 10 amps; tank-type vacuum cleaner, 5 amps; lawnmower, 9 amps; ¼ hp. motor, 6 amps; ⅓ hp., 8 amps; ¼ hp. 9 amps. No. 16 cord is better to use than No. 18. No. 12 will do a heavy job at a distance of 100 feet. If the cord is undersized, the tool can run hot and won't have full power. A small drop in voltage causes a larger drop in power.

RETRACTILE CORDS

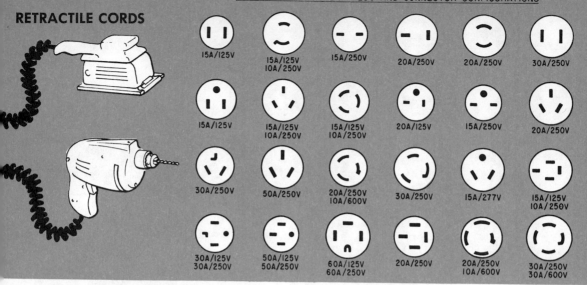

15A/125V	15A/125V 10A/250V	15A/250V	20A/250V	20A/250V	30A/250V
15A/125V	15A/125V 10A/250V	15A/125V 10A/250V	20A/125V	15A/250V	20A/250V
30A/250V	50A/250V	20A/250V 10A/600V	30A/250V	15A/277V	15A/125V 10A/250V
30A/125V 30A/250V	50A/125V 50A/250V	60A/125V 60A/250V	20A/250V	20A/250V 10A/600V	30A/250V 30A/600V

SAFETY FEATURE

Appliances and power tools with grounding plugs should be used only with three-wire grounding extension cords plugged into three-hole grounding outlets. Then if a "hot" wire inside the appliance should touch the case of the appliance, the short-circuit would be conducted to the ground through the grounding wire, not through your body. The danger is always present unless you are using double-insulated power tools. The risk is highest when working outdoors, on concrete, near grounded objects, such as plumbing or heating runs.

Ready-made extension cord sets are handy to use. They come in any length you need. Common lengths are 6, 9, 12, 15, 25, 50 and 100 feet. Unless you have plenty of use for heavy extension cords, it may pay to rent them. Most tool rental firms can supply you.

SPECIAL CORD SETS

Retractile cords—you've seen those coiled-up cords that look ready to spring. They are. They'll spring any time you pull, giving you up to six times their folded-up length. Retractile cord sets are handy on saws, drills, shop tools, power mowers, hedge clippers, spotlights, radios, TV's, lamps and all kinds of home appliances.

Interlocking plugs and taps—if a series of extension cords will be pulled around a great deal while you work, get the type with interlocking plugs and connectors.

Window air conditioners—special three-wire cord sets for window air conditioners come ready-made with plugs and taps to match. They may be had in 120- or 240-volt types. The prongs on the 240-volt plugs will not fit 120-volt outlets and vice versa.

Grounding adapters—grounding adapters enable a grounding-type cord set to be used with old-style, two-hole outlets. The grounding pigtail on the adapter should be firmly fastened to the center screw on the receptacle, but only if the outlet box is metal and is grounded through the house wiring. Otherwise the grounding lead should be extended with another wire and firmly clamped to a good ground, such as a water pipe.

Cord of any type never should be used as a substitute for permanent wiring. Don't fasten cords to the house in any way, even though staples are often sold for this purpose. Never run cords through doorways, windows, walls, ceilings, floors. Always use cord in continuous lengths from the receptacle to the appliance. Don't ever plug two cords together to make a longer one.

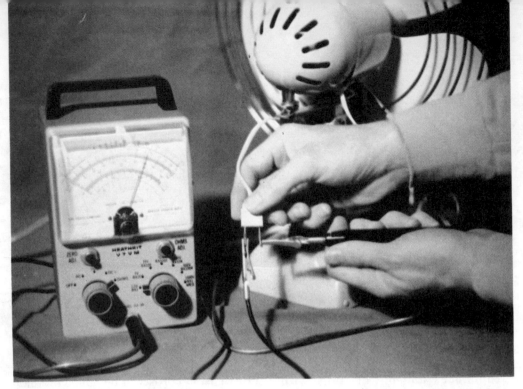

You can often save yourself the trouble of taking apart an appliance by simply check-ing out its continuity with a volt-ohm meter. It's a great aid in troubleshooting.

TROUBLESHOOTING
SMALL APPLIANCES

Toasters, mixers, irons, clocks and fans pose distinctive problems

Once you know the basics of appliance repair, as outlined in a previous chapter, you are ready to put them to use. Here are descriptions of how a num-ber of popular small appliances work and how to troubleshoot them. In each case if the appliance has a plug and a cord, that is the first place to look for trouble and has been left out of the troubleshoot-ing charts. So has repairing an appliance that shocks. This was covered pre-viously.

See the chapter on ground rules of ap-pliance repair for how to test for con-tinuity, short-circuits, open circuits and bad grounds.

Toaster — toasters last for many years without trouble. Toaster components in-clude a switch, a pop-up control and a pair of heating elements (two-slice). Most toaster troubles are mechanical, power cord or switch. Check these out first.

The mechanical action and timing of toasters varies. Some use a thermostat to end the cycle and pop up the toast. Others use windup clocks. Still others employ an electric timer. If you have pop up troubles the best way to fix it is take the toaster apart and study its ac-tion. Then you can usually tell what needs fixing.

TOASTER TROUBLESHOOTING

Trouble	Cause	Cure
Won't heat	Plug, cord, terminals	Tighten terminals. Replace or repair cord or plug if necessary.
	Faulty switch	Clean contacts with ignition file and fine emery cloth.
	Open coils	Replace coil if defective, or replace toaster.
Blows fuse	Short-circuit	Disassemble and look for wires touching each other.
Won't pop up Burns toast	Mechanical linkage faulty	Disassemble and check catches, levers and latches. Clean and lubricate with silicone grease.
	Timer faulty	Check timer operation. Clean or replace.
Toasts one side	Element burned out	Replace element.

WAFFLE IRON TROUBLESHOOTING

Trouble	Cause	Cure
Won't heat	Terminal loose	Tighten
	Faulty thermostat	Clean contact.
	Open element	Inspect for broken wire. Replace element.
Not enough heat	Low voltage	Check outlet under load for rated voltage. Find cause of low voltage and correct it.
	Terminals loose; thermostat faulty	Tighten loose terminals. Clean contacts on thermostat or replace.
Too much heat	Thermostat stuck or incorrectly adjusted	Sometimes contacts weld together. Replace if defective. Adjust thermostat (see text).
Signal lamp does not light	Burned out filament	Replace with exactly the same lamp.

Heating elements on both sides are separate circuits hooked so that current can flow through either one or both. Burned out elements can be replaced. Repair of an "open" element is too temporary to bother with. Replace it.

THERMOSTAT CONTROL

Waffle iron — a waffle iron contains upper and lower heating elements strung over ceramic insulators. They are connected so that electricity must flow through one end, then the other. If one burns out, neither will heat. A thermostat controls the heat. An indicator lamp tells when the thermostat is calling for heat.

You can get at the works on many waffle irons simply by pulling back clips that hold the griddles in place. The griddles then lift out.

Griddle temperature should run between 360 and 380 degrees F. You can adjust the temperature by pulling off the adjustment knob from its shaft, turning the shaft the way you want it to go, and pushing the knob back on in the desired position.

Coffee maker — various types of coffee makers function slightly differently. All have thermostatically controlled heating coils and often pilot lights to tell when

With housing off, check the operation of toaster's trip control. It often goes bad.

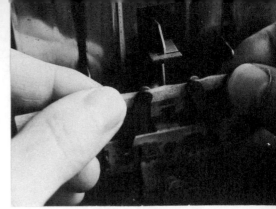

Brightening switch contacts with fine sandpaper can add years of life to a toaster.

Broken wire in toaster element makes toast brown on one side only. Replace the element.

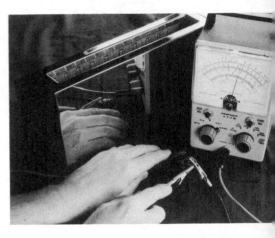

Quick way to check toaster is with an ohm test. Switch on, it should be 12-18 ohms.

they are heating. Some are automatic; in others you need to set a lever for brewing coffee or keeping coffee warm.

A high-heat element provides heat for brewing; a low-heat element for warming. On some models a switch controls high heat and a thermostat controls low heat. The opposite is found on other models. On automatic models both heats are controlled by thermostats. The electrical parts are reached by removing the base.

Inside the pot a pump—with a chamber, valve and seat—at the base sends boiling water up and over the spreader plate to brew coffee. Steam created inside the pump does it.

If the unit has ceramic insulators

where the heating element leads pass through holes, make sure they are in place when you complete your repair.

SKILLET, MIXER, BLENDER

Electric skillet—this cooking aid combines a heating element built integrally with the skillet so they can be submerged in water. If the heating element goes bad, the whole skillet may as well be replaced. A separate thermostatic control unit is used. To cook, a temperature sensing probe is inserted into the skillet. The thermostat is located in the control unit. You can easily fix it if something goes wrong. Remove the screws holding the control cover and take it off.

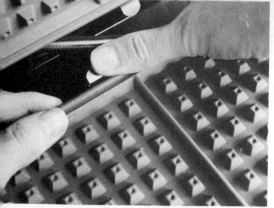

Some waffle irons are easy to service because interchangeable griddles slip out.

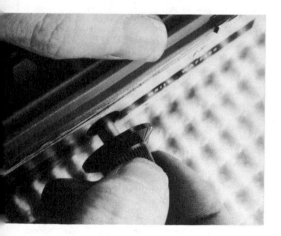

To adjust temperature on waffle iron, slip off knob and replace in different position.

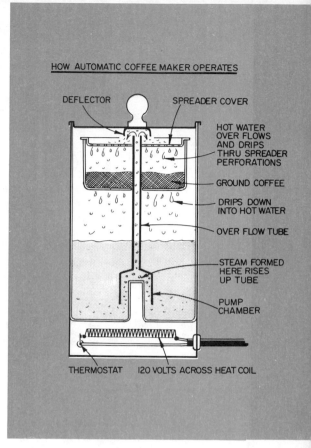

HOW AUTOMATIC COFFEE MAKER OPERATES

DEFLECTOR
SPREADER COVER
HOT WATER OVER FLOWS AND DRIPS THRU SPREADER PERFORATIONS
GROUND COFFEE
DRIPS DOWN INTO HOT WATER
OVER FLOW TUBE
STEAM FORMED HERE RISES UP TUBE
PUMP CHAMBER
THERMOSTAT   120 VOLTS ACROSS HEAT COIL

Most troubles with the control result from submerging it in water. It's supposed to be kept dry, dry, dry.

Electric mixer—the electric food mixer has a universal motor to drive a pair of beaters through a system of gears. Several types of speed controls are used; those with centrifugal-governors, tapped-fields and adjustable brushes. All must be clean and free of caked-on food to work properly. Most troubles are due to food deposits on the inner workings. Brush wear comes second.

Blender—a blender works much like a mixer except that the motor is in the base, not the upper portion.

Blenders see so little action that they

Coffee makers vary, but better ones give choice of temperature, thus, brew strength.

59

COFFEE MAKER TROUBLESHOOTING

Trouble	Cause	Cure
Won't heat	Terminals loose	Tighten
	Element burned out	Replace if "open" or get a new appliance. Some elements are tough to replace.
	Thermostat faulty	Too critical to repair. Take to shop or replace thermostat.
Won't perc or boils over	Mechanical or hydraulic faults	Check for defective stem cap, lift disc assembly, pump chamber, valve. Boiling over is often caused by a faulty valve. Replace defective parts.
	Low voltage	Correct
	Faulty thermostat	Have adjusted or replace.
Coffee won't re-turn to power bowl, or impro-per low-heat temperature	Faulty thermostat	Have adjusted or replace.
Pilot light out	Lamp filament burned out	Replace with a duplicate lamp.

ELECTRIC SKILLET TROUBLESHOOTING

Trouble	Cause	Cure
Won't heat	"Open" heating element	Replace skillet.
	Faulty thermostat	Clean contacts.
Wrong tempera-ture	Thermostat out of adjustment or dirty	Check sensing element and clean. Clean thermostat contacts. If this won't cure trouble, replace the control.

Heating element of most coffee makers can be replaced. Simply remove and buy new one.

Biggest problem with electrical skillets is when thermostat gets submerged in water.

ELECTRIC MIXER, BLENDER TROUBLESHOOTING

Trouble	Cause	Cure
Won't run	Defective speed controls	Clean contacts if necessary. Remove encrusted food. Check connections.
	Switch	Clean controls or replace if defective.
Sparks, sputters	Brushes, commutator	Check brush action, sandpaper commutator. Replace brushes if down to 3/8 inch. Clean inside of machine.
Noisy operation	Gears lack lube	Take gearbox apart and lubricate gears and motor bearings. Follow manufacturer's instructions.
Other motor trouble	Various	(See chapter on electric motor repair.)
Bent blades	Accidents	Straighten or replace blades.
Grease leakage	Worn bearings or thinned-out grease	If cleaning gearbox of old grease and repacking doesn't correct leaking at beater sockets, you need a new mixer.
Vibrates and noisy	Faulty governor	Replace governor if needed.

rarely give trouble. Check the brushes or look for a worn cord.

Electric can opener — this terrific little kitchen addition uses a small shaded-pole motor (see section on motors) and a lot of gearing down to open cans. A momentary-contact switch turns it on when you press the lever. Phillips screws hold the housing together. Take them out and you can expose the opener's workings.

About the only motor problem is caused by lack of lubrication in the bearings. A little oil should fix it. Most other troubles come from dull cutters, worn gears and similar mechanical difficulties. Clean and lubricate the exterior working parts twice a year.

Electric knife — the electric knife is a great supplement to the household. It makes the man of the house an expert meat carver. A small commutator motor runs on low DC voltage made from house current or batteries. Resistors plus a small *rectifier* provide the change in current type and voltage. A rectifier is a device that changes alternating current to direct current.

A press-*on* switch completes the circuit from cord to motor. A set of gears and a drive wheel make side-by-side knife blades reciprocate to cut.

To take apart an electric knife, simply remove the screws holding the halves of the pickle-shaped case together. All the workings will then be exposed.

CORDS WEAR OUT

Electric iron — the major problem with electric irons is cords. The ironing motions eventually wear down the wires or insulation. Replacement is the best cure. Buy a ready-made iron cord set or use heater cord and heavy-duty plugs and iron adapters. Don't forget the strain-relief spring on the iron end of the cord. A retractile cord makes a good iron cord.

An iron consists of a heating element and a thermostat. It couldn't be simpler. Faulty thermostats are more easily replaced than repaired. So are faulty heating elements.

Getting the iron apart may be difficult. Look for hidden screws, hooks or pins, usually in the handle. Try to figure out how the handle is held to the body. Push, pry or turn to see what happens. Don't force. If you can get the handle off, the rest of the repair is easy.

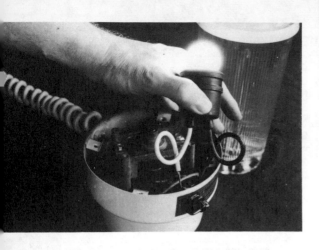

Glowing test light shows that power is getting through switch of blender's power unit.

An electric can opener will give you very little in the way of electrical problems.

Shaded-pole motors need only an occasional oiling. Follow the maker's instructions.

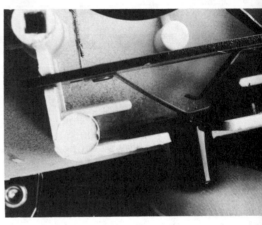

Check can opener switch to insure contacts are clean and touching when lever is moved.

Electric hair dryer—the small household size hair dryer power unit consists of switch, heating element and blower. Tubing carries the stream of hot air created in the power unit to a bonnet worn by the user. The blower draws in cool air and blows it over hot resistance wires in the heating element. Some hair dryers have two elements, one for "low" heat, another for "high." Some have varying fan speeds. A few even have thermostats to control temperature.

The case lifts off the power unit when its attaching screws are removed. Most dryer motors are the simple shaded-pole type. A few more powerful dryers use universal motors.

DUAL CONTROL BEST

Electric blanket—a resistance heating element routed around the blanket is controlled by a thermostat. The thermostat may be in the blanket. If so, it's electronic. Other blankets have the thermo-

ELECTRIC CAN OPENER TROUBLESHOOTING

Trouble	Cause	Cure
Won't run	Switch	Clean contacts.
	Terminals	Tighten
Labors	Dull cutting edges	Replace cutter.
	Dragging cutter	Remove cutter, clean all mechanical parts. Oil and assemble.
Noisy	Gears running dry	Disassemble gearbox and add grease. Replace gears if worn out.
Motor troubles	Various	(See chapter on motor repair.)

ELECTRIC KNIFE TROUBLESHOOTING

Trouble	Cause	Cure
Won't run	Switch	Clean contacts with sandpaper.
Motor runs, but blades don't move	Stripped gears	Replace gear assembly.
Motor labors, runs slowly	Brushes faulty	Check action. Sandpaper brushes and commutator. Replace brushes if worn down. Check brush wires for broken strands.
	Bearings dry	Give each bearing one drop of fine machine oil, no more.

ELECTRIC IRON TROUBLESHOOTING

Trouble	Cause	Cure
Won't heat	Faulty element, thermostat	Clean thermostat contacts. Replace faulty element.
Insufficient heat	Faulty thermostat	Clean or realign contacts. Replace, if defective. Tighten terminals.
	Low voltage	Outlet voltage should match rating of iron. A 15-volt drop lowers heating by one-third.
Improper temperature	Thermostat out of adjustment	A shop job. Take to a qualified repairman.

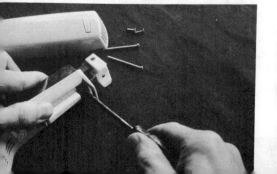

Taking apart electric knife is a matter of finding and removing holding screws.

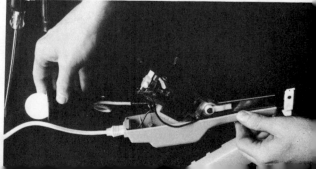

Check switch operation, putting test light on switch terminals, closing with plug in.

ELECTRIC HAIR DRYER TROUBLESHOOTING

Trouble	Cause	Cure
Won't run or heat	Switch	Replace if "open." Be sure to "tag" wires so you get them back to right terminal.
Heats, but won't run	Fan stuck	Look for fan blade catching.
	Bearing stuck	Clean and oil bearing.
Runs slowly	Bearings dragging	Oil. Align ends of motor if binding.
Won't heat	Element "open"	Replace. Match to old one.
Noisy	Fan hits housing	Loosen set-screw and reposition fan. If fan is bent, straighten it.
Hose collapsed	Mechanical damage	Slip over a broomstick and work wire coils back into place. If vinyl is cut, wrap with plastic electrician's tape or use vinyl patches.

ELECTRIC HEATING PAD, BLANKET TROUBLESHOOTING

Trouble	Cause	Cure
Won't heat	Switch	Clean contacts or replace.
	Loose terminal (blanket only)	Located inside the control box; there may be many. Tighten them all.
	Thermostat	Clean contacts or replace. Thermostats in blanket or pad may be cut out and replaced. Wire carefully.
	Open circuit in heating element	Replace entire pad or blanket.
Too hot (electronically controlled blankets only)	Bypass capacitor burned out and unit won't shut off	Located across thermostat contacts. Replace bypass capacitor.
Wrong temperature	Thermostat	Clean external thermostat or replace internal one.
	Improper use	Blankets with external thermostats must have the controls placed on a night stand or on the floor. Never rest them on or under the blanket.

ELECTRIC CLOCK TROUBLESHOOTING

Trouble	Cause	Cure
Won't run	Motor unit defective	Look through hole in motor unit to see if aluminum disc is turning. If motor has power and doesn't run, replace.
	Gears locked	Repair gears or replace clock.
Noisy or loses time	Motor worn out	Replace motor unit.
	Settled lubricant	Run clock upside down for several days to redistribute lubricant.
	Stripping gears	Replace clock.

An iron is hard to take apart. Rusty screw holding handle to base broke on this one.

Heating elements of many irons are integral with the shoe, as shown in cross-section.

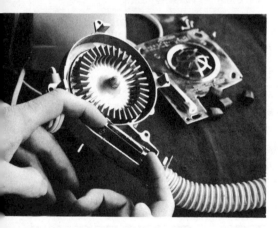

Remove screws and hair dryer's plastic cover comes off. Heating element is exposed.

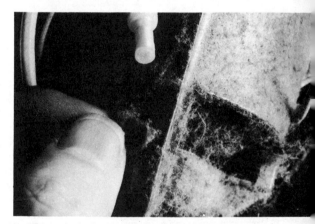

Hair dryer motor was choked with dust. Removal let it cool better and run smoother.

stat mounted in the external control box. That type measures room temperature and reacts to it. The best blankets for double beds have dual controls. Each half of the blanket is wired separately for individual control.

Blankets have magnetized thermostat contacts. Most problems are found inside the control box. Electric sheets are similar.

Electric heating pad — much like the electric blanket, a heating pad is smaller and wired to get hotter. A selector switch usually lets the user choose among three heats and *off*. A thermostat may be inside the pad wired in series with the resistance wiring. These often are troublemakers.

Electric clock — clocks draw only about 1½ watts of electricity. Powering them is a small, self-contained motor with reduction gear unit. Inside the unit a synchronous motor turns at a set speed in relation to cycles of current. Power companies are careful to control their generator speeds to keep clock time like astronomical time.

Don't try to fix a worn out or defective

ELECTRIC HEATER TROUBLESHOOTING

Trouble	Cause	Cure
Won't heat	Element "open"	Install new element of same rating as old one. See nameplate.
	Main switch	Clean contacts or replace switch.
	Tip-over switch	Check operation. Clean contacts or replace switch.
	Terminals	Clean and tighten.
Not enough heat	Low voltage	Correct
	Switch "open" on "high"	Clean contacts or replace switch.
	Thermostat	Clean contacts.
Fan trouble	Various	(See chapter on motor repair.)

FAN AND BLOWER TROUBLESHOOTING

Trouble	Cause	Cure
Motor troubles	Various	(See chapter on motor repair.)
Won't run	Switch	Replace or clean contacts.
Vibrates, noisy	Bent blades	Remove fan, lay on table and straighten blades. Check when replaced on shaft.
	Out of balance blades	Replace blades or balance.
	Squirrel cage hits housing.	Straighten squirrel cage.
Oscillating type won't oscillate	Gears worn or stripped	Replace gears or do without this feature.
	Worn clutch	Replace clutch.
Exhaust fan won't move air.	Blocked air passages	Clean out bird's nests, fix automatic doors, clean air filters.
	Dirty fan	Remove blade or squirrel cage and clean off accumulations.

CORDLESS APPLIANCE TROUBLESHOOTING

Trouble	Cause	Cure
Won't run	Batteries dead	Recharge permanent batteries or replace flashlight batteries.
	Switch	Clean contacts.
No power	Cell dead	Won't take a charge. Test individual cells to find bad one. Replace all cells.
	Needs charging	Put on charging unit for 24 hours.
No charger output	Charger module	Replace
Won't charge	Dirty charger-to-appliance contacts	Clean and bend contacts to make firmer contact with the appliance.

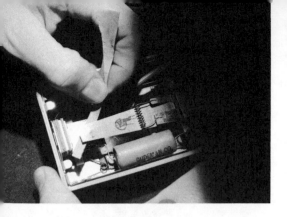

Electric blanket thermostatic control contacts are easily cleaned with sandpaper.

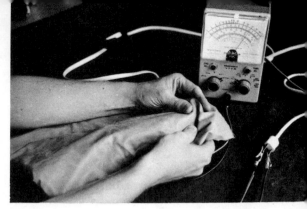

With VO meter reading resistance of heating pad, knead it. Broken wire varies it.

clock motor unit. Remove it and replace it with an exact duplicate. If a clock develops gear trouble, the whole clock may best be replaced.

Some clocks are powered by shaded-pole motors. Not much goes wrong with them either.

TIP-OVER SWITCH

Electric heater—electric heaters are used for chasing the chill from rooms. Sizes range from 500-watts up. All have resistance heating elements. Some add switch control, thermostatic control, and fans to distribute the heat. Any that might be kicked over and start a fire should incorporate a tip-over switch in the base. Whenever the base isn't resting on the floor, a plunger comes out and turns off the juice.

Replacement elements are available in a rating to match that on the heater's nameplate. Fasten the ends, then stretch the new element over the insulators. Leave enough tension in the element to hold it on the supports. The element must not touch the appliance body at any point.

Fans and blowers—fans and blowers come in many types. Both employ small electric motors—usually shaded-pole or split-phase—to turn blades or squirrel cage blowers. A blower can move air along a duct, and is used for kitchen and bathroom ventilating.

Most problems have to do with the motors. Their repairs are covered in another section.

Many fans are equipped with two-speed switches. These sometimes give trouble. So do wires on oscillating fans that get bent so many times that they break. A continuity check will tell.

RECHARGING BATTERIES

Cordless appliances—cordless appliances have self-contained batteries. These are usually rechargeable nickel-cadmium cells connected with welded-on straps. Sometimes ordinary flashlight cells are used. Rechargeable appliances come with chargers on which they rest when not in use. The appliance has a switch that connects the batteries to the DC motor.

Disassemble the appliance and take DC voltage readings with the motor running. On a 6-volt battery pack the running voltage should not drop below about 5.8 volts. If it drops to 4 volts, the batteries should be recharged. Test each cell individually under no load and full load. If any reading drops to half voltage or reverses polarity, put in a new set of batteries.

The charger unit can be tested with a DC volt meter, too. It should register 9 volts across a fully charged 6-volt battery pack. The charger module uses a silicon rectifier and resistors to make low-voltage DC out of 120-volt AC.

ELECTRICAL SAFETY

Checking for frayed wires is one of the ways to protect yourself

Even professional electricians must be reminded that electricity can start fires, burn and kill. To be safe, you must be careful. Don't think that just because house circuit voltage is only 120 volts it is relatively harmless. You may have 100-ampere service—and it takes only 1/10th of an ampere to kill. Current is what produces shock hazard. Current depends on voltage and resistance. Your body offers some resistance to current flow. How much depends mostly on how wet your skin is. If the resistance is low—wet skin, wet feet—the current flowing through body can reach the fatal 1/10th ampere.

The two standard methods of protection from shock are insulation and grounding. House electrical boxes should be grounded. Most electrical appliances are. Exceptions are those appliances with heating elements placed where you could reach the elements. This includes toasters, open-coil heaters and some rotisseries.

MOUNT SECURELY

Mount electrical boxes securely.

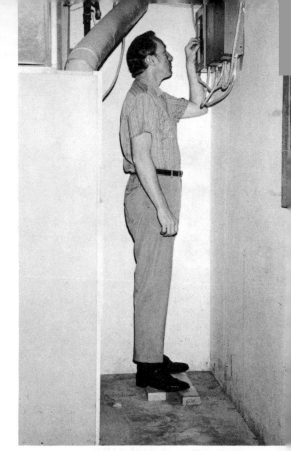

Stand on a dry board when working on any "live" electrical equipment so you are not grounded. Leather-soled shoe, concrete floor and bare hot wire can give you bad shock.

Never wire a switch across the white neutral wire. This wire must be continuous from its source to the outlet. Do all your wiring in accordance with the National Electric Code. For a copy, send $1 to the National Fire Protection Assn., 60 Batterymarch St., Boston, Mass. 02110. Some public libraries have copies.

Disconnect the electric circuit as its source before you work on it. If you aren't positive which fuse or circuit breaker does the trick, pull out the main fuse block or throw the main circuit breaker to *off*.

Always replace fuses with the proper ones for the wire size in the circuit. Usually 15-ampere fuses are it. Sometimes 20-amp. Rarely higher than that. Never

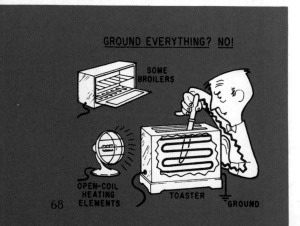

GROUND EVERYTHING? NO!

SOME BROILERS

OPEN-COIL HEATING ELEMENTS   TOASTER   GROUND

anything behind a fuse to keep it from blowing.

Realize that water and electricity don't mix. Wet hands or a wet floor greatly increase your chances for shock when working with wires or electrical tools and appliances. Don't submerge the electrical part of any appliance in water.

On the insulation side, make regular inspections around your home for frayed and deteriorated cords on tools and appliances. If you find any, don't wait to fix them. Do it right away or else cut off the plug and put the appliance aside.

PULL PLUG, NOT WIRE

When you unplug any device always pull on the plug, not the wire. Frayed cords too often result from pulling on wires. When wiring a plug, provide some means of taking the strain off the terminals, usually by tying an Underwriters knot.

Don't use a brass socket on an extension cord. Such a socket should be made of an insulation material. The socket portion of a lamp may be brass, but it should have an insulating liner.

All your major appliances, such as washing machines, freezers and refrigerators, should be grounded—unless they are already grounded through three-wire cords and three-prong plugs used in grounding outlets. A third wire attached to the frame and grounded to a water pipe will do the trick. Some washers are connected with hoses containing metal mesh. This effectively grounds the machine if the house plumbing is all metal with an underground metal entrance main.

If metal case of the tool is well grounded with low-resistance wire, the current flow under any accidental circumstances is confined between the case and the ground, and the user does not suffer. If Point 1 is grounded, the line is short-circuited and the fuse blows. If 2 is grounded, nothing happens because case is grounded already. If Junction C is grounded, line fuse blows or circuit breaker opens when switch closes.

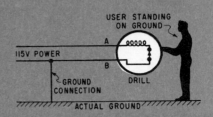

A portable drill in normal operation has the switch closed; insulation protects user.

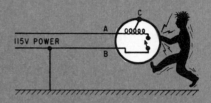

If the motor winding should ground to case at Point C, the portable drill user is usually shocked because the current will follow path through the drill casing and through the user's body to the ground and then back to the grounded power lead B as shown here.

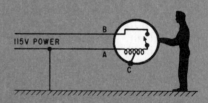

If the grounded motor of the drill should have its line plug reversed, the user will be safe—until he turns on the switch. Then, of course, he will be badly shocked.

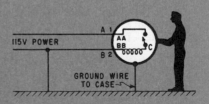

HOW TO REPLACE A RECEPTACLE OR SWITCH

It's elementary, but many people forget to turn off current first!

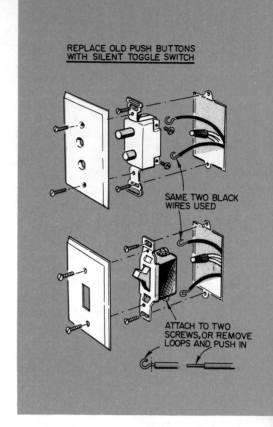

REPLACE OLD PUSH BUTTONS WITH SILENT TOGGLE SWITCH

SAME TWO BLACK WIRES USED

ATTACH TO TWO SCREWS,OR REMOVE LOOPS AND PUSH IN

Installing a new switch or receptacle in place of an old one is simple. Never try to fix a damaged device. Always replace it. First, turn off the current to the circuit supplying that outlet. This seems elementary, but there's always someone who will try to "catch it on the fly," as the pros call it. If you use an insulated screwdriver and keep yourself from being grounded at all times during the installation, you might get by without getting shocked.

But forget just once and touch a black wire — and you'll turn the power off every time after that. As an added precaution, check the wires to make sure you deadened the right circuit. Try to switch on the light, or plug a good lamp into the receptacle. You can make still another test after the bare wires have been exposed. Grasp the black wires, one at a time, by the insulation and touch them against the metal box. There should be no spark. If there is you'll have blown a fuse — but a well-spent one.

REMOVE DEVICE

With the power off, remove the outlet's cover plate. A switch plate usually has two screws; a receptacle, one. Then take out the two long screws that hold the device to the box. Gently pull the switch or receptacle from the box far enough to work on it. Loosen the terminal screws and disconnect the device.

Examine the ends of the wires to see that they are clean and not nicked. Clean if dirty. Clip them off and prepare new ends if they're nicked.

Get out the new device, which should be on hand when you begin work, and remove its attaching screws and fiber washers. Throw the washers away. A new switch should have the same number of terminals as the old one. Most have just two.

Switches are rated according to the loads they can handle. Add up the amperes of what's controlled by the switch and compare with the switch rating. This appears on the body of the switch. Most are rated for 10 amps for up to 125 volts, 5 amps up to 250 volts. To figure amperes when you know wattages, simply

Turn off current at service panel or branch panel by switching breaker or removing fuse.

Make certain that the current to the outlet is off by checking it with your test light.

Photo demonstrates removal of cover plate screw and screws at each end of the device.

Loosen terminal screws and remove the wires from device. Avoid bending wires too much.

divide by the voltage. For instance, if a switch controls a ceiling fixture with two 60-watt lamps, the total power used is 120 watts. Dividing by the voltage of 120 gives one amp of current flow. Almost any switch will handle that.

CONNECTING WIRES

Connect the switch or outlet wires the same way they came off. On a receptacle white wires must go to the chrome-plated terminal, black wires to the brass-plated one. The bare grounding wire should go from the box back to the green ground-

ing terminal. New outlets must be the three-hole grounding type unless in an ungrounded system. If the old receptacle was not of the grounding type, you'll either have to install a grounding wire from the green terminal to the metal outlet box or make sure that the metal mounting tabs of the new receptacle make firm contact with the metal box. A grounding wire, if installed, should be screwed to the back of the metal box. Don't install a grounding receptacle on a porcelain or plastic outlet box without connecting a grounding wire. Don't install one at all on an ungrounded electri-

If a wire is nicked or weakened by bending, cut it off. Strip insulation from new end.

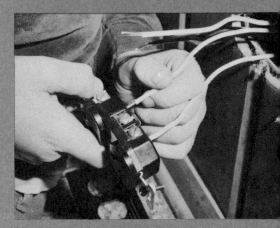

Slip wires into push-in device. White wires go to chrome terminal side, black to brass.

A push-in device has 4 or 8 holes for the wires. Strip each wire as shown on gauge.

Drill for self-tapping screw if there's no hole for attaching a ground in metal box.

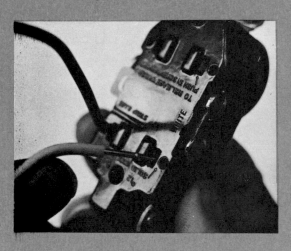

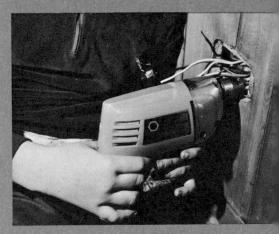

cal system. In that case use a two-hole nongrounding receptacle.

Wires connected to a switch are black or red. This is because a switch breaks only the "hot" side of the circuit. That's all it takes to stop the flow of electricity in both sides. Connect the leads the way they came off. Switch terminals are brass-plated. This is a reminder that only dark wires are wired to switches, never white ones. There's an exception in new work but the white wire must be painted black. That situation is described later. When you connect a switch make sure the *on-off* lettering is right side up.

All leads with loops should be connected so that the loops turn the same

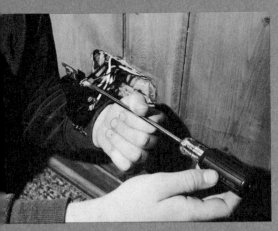

Connect bare grounding wire to box back and to green grounding terminal of receptacle.

Push device back into its box, arranging wires comfortably inside to avoid strain.

Install the screws that hold outlet to wall. Break off plaster ears if they get in way.

Grounding test is touching probes of 100-watt test light from hot hole to ground hole.

way as the screws do in tightening them.

PLASTER EARS

Lay the device back into the box, taking care to arrange the wires in the box to relieve strain. Install the two long screws and draw the device tight to the box. If the metal tabs at either end called

plaster ears interfere with a flush installation, break them off with pliers.

Plumb the device before you tighten all the way. A small level is handy, or step back and level it by eye. Install the cover plate, a new one if the old one is beat up. Turn on the power and try your newly wired project.

In designing your kitchen, it's possible to get metal plug-mold raceways that look much like an ordinary baseboard, yet allow you to plug into them at intervals around the room.

HOW TO ADD NEW LIGHTS AND OUTLETS

Updating the electrical system in

your house greatly modernizes it

A home that has too few lights and convenience outlets can be electrically up-dated without too much effort. The Saturday morning electrician can tackle one added outlet, one added light at a time and soon have all the conveniences of modern wiring. New electrical lights and outlets are merely extensions of the present electrical system. The system must, however, be adequate to carry the load (see the chapter on wiring an addition or vacation home). If your electrical system measures up, you can add new receptacles and lights wherever you need them.

Modern convenience dictates that there be a wall receptacle every 12 feet around the room on long walls, plus an outlet on each wall under 12 feet long. Outlets are needed at 4-foot intervals in kitchens. One should be at each work area. You also need at least one outlet by the mirror in the bathroom. Older houses may have only one outlet per wall, or even one per room.

You may add outlets in between or put new outlets on walls that don't already have them. Study your present extension cord system to see where new outlets are most needed. Then put them there.

Outdoors, a weatherproof outlet is needed near the front entrance and two are needed close to any outdoor living

PROPER HOUSE LIGHTING

ROOM	GENERAL ILLUMINATION		TASK LIGHTING		REMARKS
	Bulb	Fluorescent	Bulb	Fluorescent	
Living, dining room	150W	60-80W	40-150W	15-40W	For small living rooms
Bedroom	200W				
Bath	150W	80W	2 of 60W	2 of 20W	Task lights on both sides of mirror
Kitchen	150-200W	60-80W	60W	10W per foot of counter	Fixture over eating area or sink-150W bulb, 60W fluorescent
Halls, service	75W	32W			Plus low-wattage night lights
Stairway	40W				Shielded fixtures at top and bottom controlled by 3-way switch
Outdoor, entry and access	40W				Wall brackets aimed down
Hall entrance	120W	60W			
Outdoor, yard	100-150W projector				Controlled from garage and house
Laundry	2 of 150W	2 of 80W			Placed over washing and ironing areas
Workshop	150W	80W	60W	10W per foot of bench	Task lights aimed at machines
Garage	2 of 100W				On ceiling, center of each side of car

area. The garage needs at least one outlet per car.

Light is needed in the modern home for safety and convenience, both indoors and outdoors. For the safety of your family and guests there should be ample light from street and driveway to the entrance, as well as throughout the house interior from attic to basement. Fluorescent lamps can be of a lower wattage than incandescent bulbs because they put out more light per watt.

ARCHITECTURAL LIGHTING

Architectural or built-in lights give the general illumination a room needs if table and floor lamps are not used. Built right into the walls or ceilings and switched from the wall, the lighting units can be made to harmonize with the room. Sometimes the unit barely shows behind an opening in the ceiling. Architectural

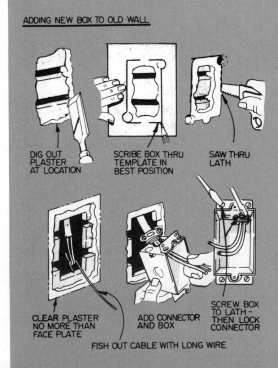

ADDING NEW BOX TO OLD WALL

DIG OUT PLASTER AT LOCATION

SCRIBE BOX THRU TEMPLATE IN BEST POSITION

SAW THRU LATH

CLEAR PLASTER NO MORE THAN FACE PLATE

ADD CONNECTOR AND BOX

SCREW BOX TO LATH - THEN LOCK CONNECTOR

FISH OUT CABLE WITH LONG WIRE

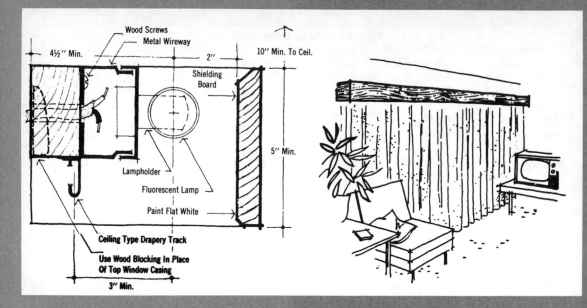

Labels in figure:
- Wood Screws
- Metal Wireway
- 4½″ Min.
- 2″
- 10″ Min. To Ceil.
- Shielding Board
- 5″ Min.
- Lampholder
- Fluorescent Lamp
- Paint Flat White
- Ceiling Type Drapery Track
- Use Wood Blocking In Place Of Top Window Casing
- 3″ Min.

Valances are used at windows to provide uplight that reflects off ceiling for general room lighting, and down-light for drapery accent. There must be at least three inches from lamp center to drapery track to insure that draperies will be uniformly lighted. When the lights are closer to the ceiling than 10 inches, use a closed top to prevent ceiling brightness and glare.

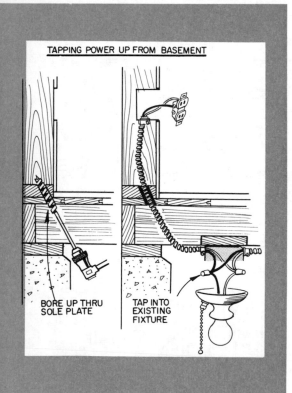

TAPPING POWER UP FROM BASEMENT

BORE UP THRU SOLE PLATE

TAP INTO EXISTING FIXTURE

lighting makes a wall or ceiling the main source of light. The basic architectural lighting units for walls—valance, cornices, wall brackets—are formed of three basic parts: Baked white enamel channels, fluorescent tubes to fit the channels, and a faceboard. You can buy the whole unit ready to install, or buy only the channels and tubes and make the faceboard to go with them.

A wall switch at the entrance to each room should control at least one light or fixture in the room. Then you'll never have to walk into a dark room. The light can be a ceiling or wall fixture or a lamp that's plugged into a switched receptacle. Multiple switches are needed at all entrances more than 10 feet apart, as well as at the head and foot of stairways.

ADDING OUTLETS

The installation of new electrical outlets (here *outlets* means lights as well as receptacles) is somewhat different in an older house than in a new one. Holes must be cut for the new boxes. Cables have to be pulled through the walls, floors, and ceilings. Often you must cut

MAXIMUM WIRES IN A BOX

Box type	Box size	No. 14	No. 12	No. 10
Junction box	3¼"×1½" oct.	5	4	4
Junction box	4"×1½" oct.	8	7	6
Multi-purpose box	4"×4"×1½"	11	10	9
Switch box	2"×3"×1½"	3	3	3
Switch box	2"×3"×2½"	6	5	5
Handy box	2"×4"×1½"	5	4	4

access holes in walls and ceilings to fish cables through them.

The first step is to locate the new outlets and cut openings for the boxes. Always locate a new outlet between framing members. Find studs or joists by tapping or with a stud-locator. The best box location is a spot 4 to 5 inches from a joist or stud. Put switches 48 inches above the floor, receptacles 12 inches. Wall light fixtures should be 66 to 70 inches above the floor. If you can, use large 2×3-inch boxes that are 2½ inches deep.

If you are cutting into a lath-and-plaster wall, center your box opening over one full oath and parts of two others. This leaves good mounting for the top and bottom of the box. Use the template shown in the drawing, tracing it onto the wall. Drill four half-inch holes as shown. Then saw out the plug with a hacksaw blade. The blade's teeth should point toward you to cut on the *pull* stroke.

GETTING POWER

The next step is to locate a source of electricity. The easiest place to tap power is in the basement or attic, immediately below or above the new outlet. You can also bring power from a wall receptacle or from a light circuit. When tapping into lights and switches you'll have to open the box to tell whether there is a neutral (white) wire. Either the light or the switch will have it.

When you find a convenient box where power can be tapped, make sure it doesn't already hold its limit of wires (see Chart). if it does, you'll have to go elsewhere. The last receptacle box in a circuit usually contains only two wires,

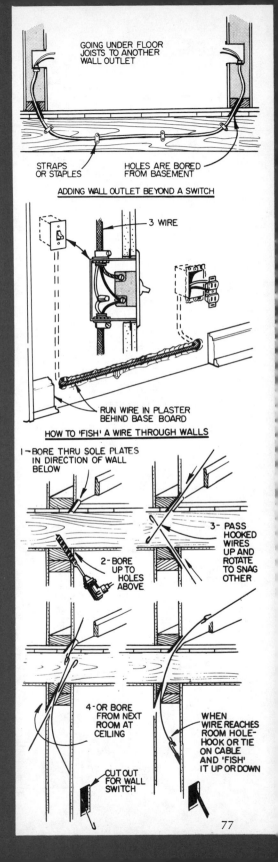

GOING UNDER FLOOR JOISTS TO ANOTHER WALL OUTLET

STRAPS OR STAPLES

HOLES ARE BORED FROM BASEMENT

ADDING WALL OUTLET BEYOND A SWITCH

3 WIRE

RUN WIRE IN PLASTER BEHIND BASE BOARD

HOW TO 'FISH' A WIRE THROUGH WALLS

1 – BORE THRU SOLE PLATES IN DIRECTION OF WALL BELOW

2 - BORE UP TO HOLES ABOVE

3 - PASS HOOKED WIRES UP AND ROTATE TO SNAG OTHER

4 - OR BORE FROM NEXT ROOM AT CEILING

WHEN WIRE REACHES ROOM HOLE- HOOK OR TIE ON CABLE AND 'FISH' IT UP OR DOWN

CUT OUT FOR WALL SWITCH

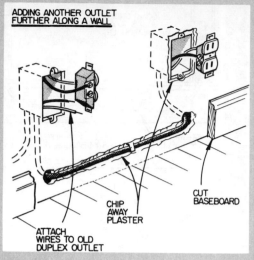

CHIP
AWAY
PLASTER

CUT
BASEBOARD

ATTACH
WIRES TO OLD
DUPLEX OUTLET

IF BOXES MEET BEHIND WALL—

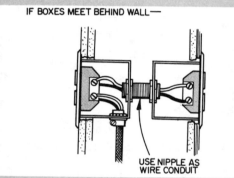

USE NIPPLE AS
WIRE CONDUIT

RUNNING CABLE AROUND A DOOR FRAME

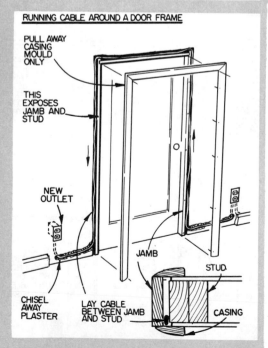

PULL AWAY
CASING
MOULD
ONLY

THIS
EXPOSES
JAMB AND
STUD

NEW
OUTLET

JAMB

STUD

CHISEL
AWAY
PLASTER

LAY CABLE
BETWEEN JAMB
AND STUD

CASING

ADDING FIXTURE FROM WITHIN ATTIC

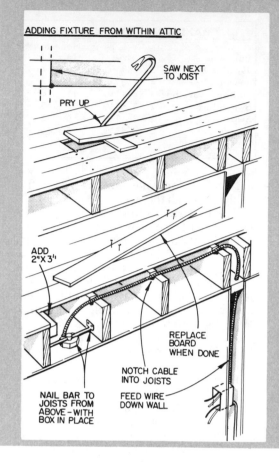

SAW NEXT
TO JOIST

PRY UP

ADD
2"X 3"

REPLACE
BOARD
WHEN DONE

NOTCH CABLE
INTO JOISTS

NAIL BAR TO
JOISTS FROM
ABOVE – WITH
BOX IN PLACE

FEED WIRE
DOWN WALL

leaving room for two more. Find it by removing cover plates and peering inside.

Plan your cable route for the easiest fishing. That is the problem in adding new outlets. Cost of cable and other factors take a back seat to easing the cable installation. Do your fishing with baling wire and an electrician's fish tape. Because a fish tape is apt to be quite springy, you may prefer the baling wire method.

You can even bring power from the entrance panel if that is easier. Start a new circuit, if there is one left.

Sometimes the easiest route for a new cable is behind a baseboard or directly across a wall. Chisel holes through the wall to feed the cables and cut a groove along the wall between holes. Fish the cable, lay it in the groove and finish the wiring job. Afterward, replaster the wall

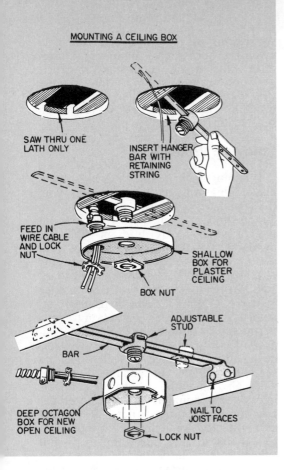

MOUNTING A CEILING BOX

SAW THRU ONE LATH ONLY

INSERT HANGER BAR WITH RETAINING STRING

FEED IN WIRE CABLE AND LOCK NUT

SHALLOW BOX FOR PLASTER CEILING

BOX NUT

ADJUSTABLE STUD

BAR

DEEP OCTAGON BOX FOR NEW OPEN CEILING

NAIL TO JOIST FACES

LOCK NUT

and repaint or hang new wallpaper. Save the old wallpaper if you can by slitting it with a razor blade and folding a flap of it up out of the way.

Replastering won't be necessary if the cable route goes behind a baseboard. Merely replace the base molding to cover the openings. If the cable interferes with the base molding's fit, chisel it out on the back.

CABLE HOOKUP

Turn off the power. Remove the proper knockout from the existing box and fish one end of your cable into it from behind the wall. The cable connector—either for nonmetallic or armored cable—should be installed on the cable before it is fed behind the wall. You'll have to drill a larger hole than for the cable alone to pass the connector. Fish

the cable's lead wires into the knock-out opening. Work the connector through the knockout until you can screw on the locknut and tighten it.

For switches and receptacles, remove the knockout from a box designed for remodeling work. These have side clamps or other means of fastening the box into the wall opening. Insert the cable through the knockout, make up the connection and install the box in the wall according to directions packed with it. Make up all your wires and devices, and the job is ready for try-out.

Back-to-back outlets in the same wall can be wired by drilling matching holes and connecting across them with conduit or a threaded rigid conduit nipple with locknuts and bushings. Every length of rigid conduit needs a bushing screwed on to cover the raw end.

CEILING BOXES

If you have access above the ceiling to mount a box for a light fixture, there's no problem. But if you must work from the room side of the ceiling, use a special, shallow round ceiling box with hanger. Cut away the ceiling surface to the size of the box. Center the opening on a lath if there is one. Cut away only the middle lath. Do it carefully, without breaking up plaster around it. Insert the special hanger (see drawing). Center the hanger in the opening and install the box and locknut after fastening the cable to it with a connector. The new fixture may be hung from the box.

Fixtures mount to boxes in various ways. Some boxes have threaded fixture studs. Others hold with straps. Straps may be held to a stud or to threaded tabs on the box. Still others have threaded nipples. Some boxes make use of a strap with an extension nipple holding the fixture. A cap screws onto the nipple, drawing the fixture's canopy to the wall or ceiling.

Recessed fixtures are installed by sawing out an open space for the fixture between joists. Wood mounting strips are placed above the opening across the lath. Install the fixture box in the opening af-

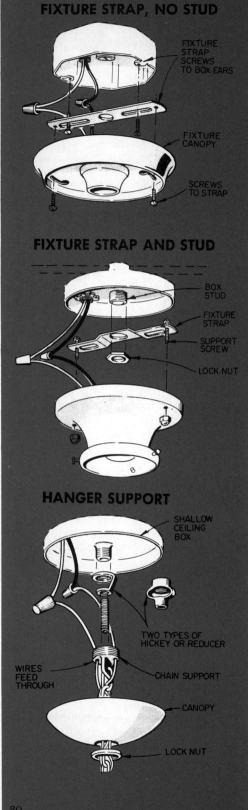

FIXTURE STRAP, NO STUD

FIXTURE STRAP SCREWS TO BOX EARS

FIXTURE CANOPY

SCREWS TO STRAP

FIXTURE STRAP AND STUD

BOX STUD

FIXTURE STRAP

SUPPORT SCREW

LOCK NUT

HANGER SUPPORT

SHALLOW CEILING BOX

TWO TYPES OF HICKEY OR REDUCER

WIRES FEED THROUGH

CHAIN SUPPORT

CANOPY

LOCK NUT

ter making up the cable to it. Some recessed fixtures have mounting straps. Others fasten with screws into the joists or wood strips. Your code may require that a recessed fixture have a separate junction box attached to it. Others don't. Check.

SURFACE WIRING

If fishing wires behind the walls, floors and ceilings of your house scares you, then use surface wiring. If you paint it to match the wall, you'll scarcely notice it after a while. Many different types are available. Local codes may restrict what you may use. You can get surface wiring in plastic or metal. Metal is harder to install but is more permanent. Most codes approve it. What's more, if properly installed, it offers every protection to your wiring that conduit does, including full ground continuity. Metal raceways are designed to go straight as well as around corners in every imaginable direction. They also have end fittings for connecting conduit, nonmetallic or armored cable, or to existing outlets. Raceways come in plug- or light-socket moldings, too, if that's what you want. For a full selection see your dealer.

One kind of surface wiring system uses plastic sockets, receptacles and switch components — as many as you like. These are connected to a special dual-purpose plastic cable. This is not "zip" cord or anything like it. The heavy plastic covered cable runs unobtrusively along the baseboard and one end is plugged into the nearest wall outlet. The system is recommended for putting an extra light in the garage, workshop, pantry or closet or other similar locations or for locating an extra receptacle anywhere you need it. Check your Code.

FANCY SWITCHING

When you first look at the wiring diagrams for three- and four-way switching systems, they appear complex. They're not, once you understand them. Three-way switches are used mostly for controlling lights from two different loca-

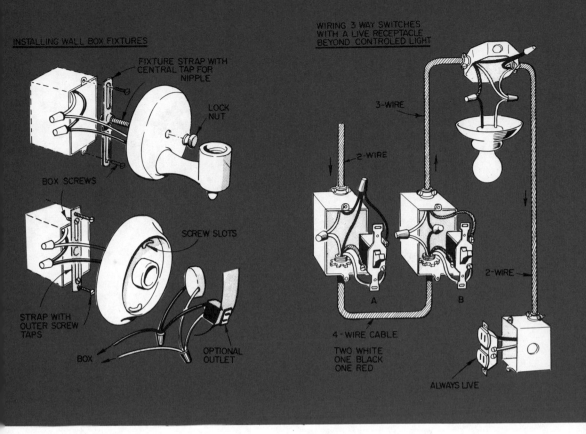

FIXTURE STRAP WITH CENTRAL TAP FOR NIPPLE

LOCK NUT

BOX SCREWS

SCREW SLOTS

STRAP WITH OUTER SCREW TAPS

BOX

OPTIONAL OUTLET

WIRING 3 WAY SWITCHES WITH A LIVE RECEPTACLE BEYOND CONTROLED LIGHT

3-WIRE

2-WIRE

2-WIRE

A

B

4 - WIRE CABLE

TWO WHITE ONE BLACK ONE RED

ALWAYS LIVE

tions—for instance, garage and house. Four-way switches are used when three or more switching locations are desired.

Use one four way switch for each switching location more than the first two. The drawing shows hookup. Notice that three-wire cable is used in some runs, two-wire in others. The *A* and *B* terminals are the chrome-plated ones. The red and white wires should be connected to these The *C* terminals are for black wires. The white wire from the switch must always be painted black at both the switch and the outlet. Switch hookup is the only time a white wire is connected to a black one. Then it has to be painted black. Do it.

Where four-wire cable is shown, use a pair of two-wire cables coming into the boxes through different knockouts. Be sure you use boxes large enough to hold all the wires.

When using the chart to figure how many wires a box can hold, wires from the fixture to wires in the box are not counted. In conduit work, wires often enter a box and leave it again without being spliced inside. Such a wire is counted only as one wire, not two. If there is a fixture stud, or set of cable clamps inside the box, deduct one wire. The total deduction from all these sources, however, is only one, no matter how many there are. Cable connectors require no deduction. Subtract also for a switch, receptacle or group of them that fits into the box. Grounding wires are not counted. These are National Electric Code limitations set down for your safety.

Compact heat pump wrings heat or cold from the outside air, whichever is needed for home.

ELECTRICITY:
THE TURNED-ON HEAT

The thermostat, as part of relay system, controls room temperature

Electric heat is different. Electricity is not only a "fuel," it is also a kind of heating. As a fuel, electricity can be used to heat water or air in a furnace or boiler the same way that gas and fuel oil do. It can also be routed around to resistance wires or panels. Used in this way, it is a heating system all by itself.

Electric heat is coming on strong. Every year more homes use it. Electric

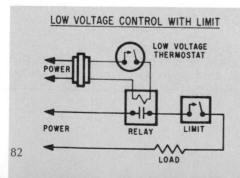

LOW VOLTAGE CONTROL WITH LIMIT

LOW VOLTAGE
THERMOSTAT

POWER

POWER

RELAY   LIMIT

82

LOAD

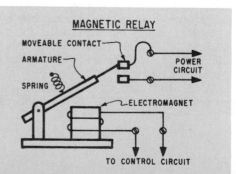

MAGNETIC RELAY

MOVEABLE CONTACT

ARMATURE

SPRING

POWER
CIRCUIT

ELECTROMAGNET

TO CONTROL CIRCUIT

heat is quiet, safe, convenient. And you'll never run out of fuel unless, of course, there is a power failure. Then other heating systems won't work either. Their blowers, pumps and controls are electrical.

The only drawback to electricity for heating seems to be its cost. Rates are coming down, however. This may account for the steady gains in usage. With a heating rate of 1½ cents per kilowatt hour or less, electric heat may be worth considering when building a home or adding onto one. Utilities usually give special low rates to electric heat users. Ask your utility how much electric heat would cost per kilowatt hour. To take advantage of electric heat, you'll probably need 200-ampere, 240-volt electrical service.

BEST METHODS

The best methods of electric heat at present are the ceiling resistance cable, which is embedded in the ceiling; plasterboard resistance panels containing a conductive film; vinyl sheets containing a copper mesh conductor in nylon netting; baseboard units mounted at the floor along outside walls; electric central heating using resistance coils instead of an oil or gas furnace; and the heat pump, which wrings heat out of outdoor air, concentrates it and brings it indoors. In summer, a heat pump's operation can be reversed to cool the house. (For more information on these systems see the PRACTICAL HANDYMAN guide on plumbing and heating.)

Radiant electric heat has a big advantage in that each room can be on a separate heating circuit controlled by its own thermostat. Then the living room can be kept warmer than a recreation room. A bedroom can be kept cool or however the occupant likes it. Rooms that get morning or afternoon sun can be held at an even temperature all day long because their temperatures are individually controlled.

Electric radiant systems are said to make the house feel like a warm spring day by blanketing the room with a warm glow.

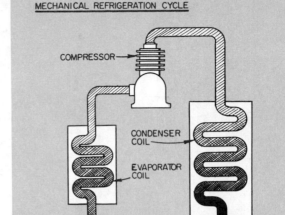

MECHANICAL REFRIGERATION CYCLE

COMPRESSOR

CONDENSER COIL

EVAPORATOR COIL

EXPANSION POINT

RECEIVER

RELAY SYSTEM

Each room thermostat—or area thermostat, if preferred—operates a relay in a central heating control cabinet. A relay is an electrically operated switch. The control panel is usually mounted near the service panel and fed from it by heavy wires. Each relay switches power to the room heating circuit on and off as directed by the thermostat. Another device cycles the heating circuits to level power flow during off-peak periods. In this way one, then another, then still another heating circuit is energized to keep them from calling for current all at once and shutting off all at once.

Because the circuitry is different from wiring and little information is available, wiring an electric heating system had best be handled by a professional. As with any electrical wiring, don't attempt it unless you understand fully what you are doing.

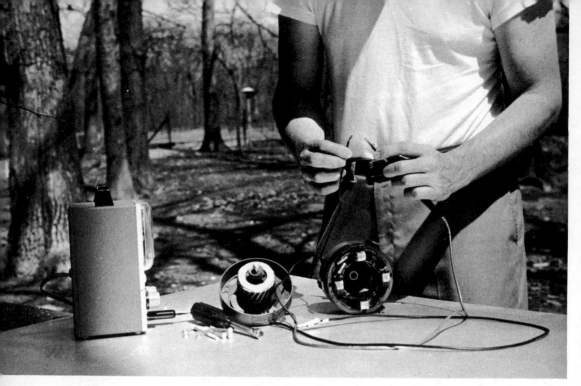

ELECTRICAL MOTOR REPAIR

Split-phase, capacitors and universals can be fixed at home by you

Chances are you have quite a few electrical motors around the house. You could well have 25 motors working for you and not realize it. Motors serve your heating system, saw wood, drill metal, chill milk, tell time, play records, dry clothes, dry hair, brush teeth, pump water, trim hedges, mix food, polish floors, freeze foods, blow air and do lots of other jobs.

The reason motors don't seem too numerous is that they aren't squeaky wheels. If a motor does give trouble you don't have to take it lying down. There are many things you can do without going to a repair shop.

Nearly all motors used around the house develop less than one horsepower, often much less. Most work on 120 volts. Some also can be wired to work on 240. Such household motors are all AC induction motors. Most are single-phase—that is they are designed to run on single-phase house current. Single-phase induction motors are further grouped as split-phase, capacitor, shaded-pole and repulsion-induction. Series, or universal motors, are not limited to single-phase current, or AC either. They will run on AC or DC single-phase or poly-phase.

Poly-phase electricity, usually three-phase, is used by industry and large farms because of its tremendous ability to turn high horsepower motors. Four wires are required, three for the three phases plus a neutral. Current alternations in each of three wires take place slightly out of phase with each other. The *B* phase is one-third cycle behind the *A* phase. The *C* phase is one-third cycle behind the *B* phase and two-thirds cycle behind the *A* phase.

MOTOR TYPES

Don't let all the motor types throw you. There are far more similarities than differences. And what's more, most motors suffer the same illnesses, when they get sick.

First a basic understanding of the common motor types, then how to fix them.

Split-phase—most low-starting-torque motorized appliances use split-phase motors. Fans, blowers, washing machines, heating plants all use them. Chief identifying feature of the split-

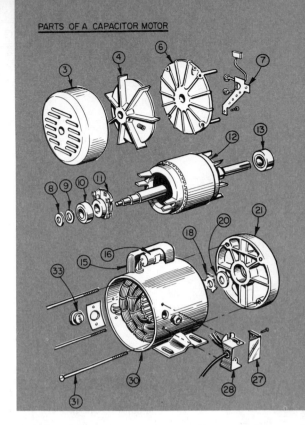

PARTS OF MOTOR: 3) cover; 4) fan; 6) end bell; 7) switch contact plate; 8) and 9) end-plate washer; 10) and 13) bearings; 11) centrifugal switch; 12) squirrel cage rotor; 15) capacitor cover; 16) capacitor; 18) and 20) end-play washers; 21) end bell; 27) and 28) wiring box; 30) body and field; 31) assembly bolt; and 33) thermal overload protector.

Two or four through-the-motor bolts hold the motor assembly together. Remove them and motor will separate into 2 or 3 pieces.

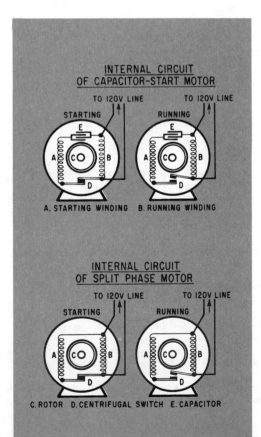

INTERNAL CIRCUIT
OF CAPACITOR-START MOTOR

TO 120V LINE   TO 120V LINE
STARTING   RUNNING

E   E

A (C O) B   A (C O) B

D   D

A. STARTING WINDING   B. RUNNING WINDING

INTERNAL CIRCUIT
OF SPLIT PHASE MOTOR

TO 120V LINE   TO 120V LINE
STARTING   RUNNING

A (C O) B   A (C O) B

D   D

C. ROTOR   D. CENTRIFUGAL SWITCH   E. CAPACITOR

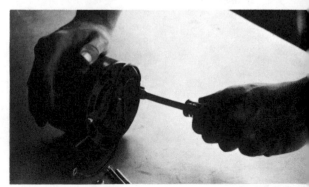

TROUBLESHOOTING ELECTRIC MOTORS

Trouble	Cause	Cure
Won't start, makes no sound	Power off, fuse blown, switch off, receptacle faulty	Plug something else into the receptacle to see if there is power to the motor.
	Faulty cord	Fix plug, cord, loose internal connection at terminal board.
	Capacitor open, burned out windings, overload protector tripped	Have capacitor checked. Replace it defective. Look and smell for charred insulation. Get new motor if burned out. Check for loose terminal or broken internal wire. Test windings individually for continuity. Push reset button on manual reset type. Wait for automatic type to reset as motor cools.
	Sticking brushes	Check brush movement and spring pressure. Clean or replace springs or brushes if necessary.
Won't start, but hums or tries to start.	Low voltage	Find cause and correct.
	Centrifugal switch not closing	Remove motor from load, turn on switch to motor. Spin shaft by hand. If it starts then or if motor starts itself only in certain rotor positions, clean switch and sandpaper points. Check shaft for more than 0.030 inch end-play. Add fiber washers to end of shaft opposite switch to reduce excessive end-play and make switch close. Minimum end-play should be 0.005 inches. Check centrifugal switch for worn parts.
	Capacitor failure, shorted, open or lost capacitance	Have capacitor tested. Replace if necessary.
	Stator windings, grounded or shorted	Test for grounds. If this is okay have motor tested for amperage draw, and compare it to that shown on nameplate. Replace faulty windings or whole motor.
	Bearings tight	Turn shaft by hand. If tight or frozen, oil. If still tight, remove and clean bearings and oil. Replace bearings if necessary.
	Overloaded	Check driven unit for overload.
	Rotor rubs stator	Check for worn bearings or cracked end frame. Look for rust and corrosion. Clean and coat with thin lacquer.
Overheats, hot or smoking	Low voltage	(See same cause under "Won't Start, hums," above.)
	Centrifugal switch not opening	Check governor weight action. Check spring action.
	Stator windings grounded or shorted	(See same cause under "Won't Start, hums," above.)
	Bearings tight	(See same cause under "Won't Start, hums," above.)
	Overloaded	Check driven unit for binding. Use larger motor.
	Dirty motor	Blow out dust and air passages. Clean inside of motor to permit better cooling.
	Rotor rubs stator	(See same cause under "Won't Start, hums," above.)

TROUBLESHOOTING ELECTRIC MOTORS

Trouble	Cause	Cure
Brushes spark	Short-circuit or open circuit in rotor windings	Check for solder or metal between commutator bars. Check for open or grounded windings. Have shop check amp-draw. Replace parts or whole motor.
	Worn or sticking brushes	Check brush operation. Clean or install new brushes. Check tension of brush springs. Replace if necessary.
	Rough commutator	Clean with fine sandpaper. Check mica for being too high. Cut down with hacksaw blade, if necessary.
	Overloaded	Decrease load.
	Poor brush fit	Put sandpaper around commutator under brushes and rotate shaft to fit brush to commutator.
Excessive bearing wear	Improper mounting	Check and correct misalignment and improper belt tension.
	Poor lubrication	Follow manufacturer's recommended lubrication schedule. Don't overlubricate.
Noisy operation	Loose parts	Check and tighten loose parts, such as terminal cover plate, capacitor housing, fan, baffle, worn switch parts, etc.
	Excessive end-play	Add thrust washers. Use those sold for that motor.
	Worn rubber mounts	Replace if gummy or hard and brittle.
	Loose pulley or coupling	Tighten or replace.
	Improper mounting	Remount to correct misalignment or loose mounting.
	Unbalance in pulley or motor	Check with motor disconnected from load. Get it balanced or replace faulty part. Bent shaft can cause unbalance too. Replace rotor.
	Dirt in air gap between rotor and stator	Remove rotor and clean both.
	Shorts in running windings	Have amperage-draw checked.
Motor lacks power	Low voltage	(See same cause under "Won't Start, hums," above.)
	Wrong voltage	Motor wired to run on 240 volts is sluggish on 120 volts. See workshop wiring chapter for how to change voltage on some motors.
	Starting windings grounded or shorted	(See "Stator windings grounded or shorted" under "Won't Start, hums," above.) Replace windings or whole motor.
	Capacitor shorted	Have capacitor checked at shop.
	Bearings tight, not enough end-play in shaft	Spin shaft to check for free-turning. Clean and oil bearings, install thrust washers as necessary.
Motor shocks when touched	Stator grounded	(See "Stator windings grounded or shorted" under "Won't Start hums," above.) Don't use motor until repaired.
	Static electricity	Check belt tension; correct if necessary. Install grounding lead between motor frame and a good ground.

Squirrel cage rotor has no windings, commutator or other complicated parts. It's simple. Eddy currents make rotor revolve.

Rotor of a universal motor is wire-wound. The circuits are fastened to copper bars of a commutator at one end (right) of rotor.

Split-phase, capacitor motor has centrifugal device on rotor to work switch contacts on end bell. Check collar for free action.

Excessive end-play is corrected by adding the right size washer to the rotor shaft on the side opposite the centrifugal switch.

phase motor is its *rotor*, the part that revolves when the motor runs. The split-phase rotor is a nonwound, or "squirrel cage" type. The *stator*, or nonrevolving outside poles, has windings of wire embedded in slots of a laminated steel core.

There are two sets of windings, the main or *running* windings and the phase or *starting* windings.

The sets of windings are connected through a centrifugal switch as shown in the schematic.

The windings are displaced in magnetic position from the running windings to create a two-phase field. This two-phase field gets the rotor spinning quickly. The motor would not start without the starting windings. It would run if the shaft were given a spin. It would go in either direction, once started that way.

After the rotor reaches a predetermined speed, the magnetic boost is no longer needed. A switch actuated by a weight on the rotor cuts the starting windings out of the circuit. The motor

Remove all the field coil leads from motor terminals. Test field coils one at a time for resistance with VO meter on low ohms.

Before handling a capacitor, discharge it through test light. Capacitor can hold its charge long time and still give you a jolt.

Check each lead to see that its circuit is not grounded to the motor frame. Set meter on high ohms. Needle should stay on infinity.

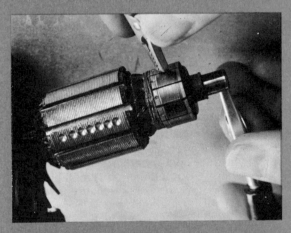

Ground test rotor by touching one lead of VO meter to shaft and moving other around commutator. Needle should stay at infinity.

then operates as a single-phase induction motor.

Most split-phase motor problems center around operation of the centrifugal switch or bearing problems that develop from improper lubrication.

LIKE SPLIT-PHASE

Capacitor — nearly all capacitor motors you'll run into are of the capacitor-start type. Other kinds of capacitor motors differ somewhat.

A capacitor-start motor is similar to,

but a step up from, the split-phase motor. It has a metal housing on the frame to hold a large capacitor or condenser. A capacitor is an electrical component that cushions any rapid change in current. The capacitor is wired in the path of the electrical current to the starting windings. (See drawing.) It effectively reduces current during starting to less than half that required by a split-phase motor. Moreover, it produces a greater torque or twisting force during startup.

Capacitor motors are used for hard-

CONNECTION DIAGRAM
SPLIT-PHASE AND
CAPACITOR-START MOTORS

PHASE

LINE

SWITCH

MAIN

CAPACITOR
(C.S. MOTORS)

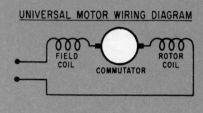

UNIVERSAL MOTOR WIRING DIAGRAM

FIELD
COIL

COMMUTATOR

ROTOR
COIL

to-start loads or low-starting-amp requirements. Compressors, large fans, water pumps and blowers have them. So do many shop tools. They are not as common as straight split-phase motors because of their higher cost.

FOR LIGHT DUTY

Shaded-pole—the shaded pole motor has an interesting name, given to it because of the way it works. Low-torque, light-duty motors are sometimes of this design. You find them on small blowers, ceiling fans and some small appliances, such as phonographs.

A loop of heavy copper strap or wire replaces the starting winding. This loop is mounted in the face of steel stator pole laminations. A groove is cut in the laminations (see drawing) so that about one-third of the pole's laminations are encircled by the copper loop. An alternating current induces a "shading" current in the copper loop that makes the magnetic field shift across the pole, first away from, then toward the loop. The shifting field makes the rotor turn along with the weak rotating magnetic field. A shaded-pole motor has no centrifugal switch and not much else to go wrong. They run and run, as long as the bearings are lubricated.

Repulsion-induction—more accurately named repulsion-start induction-run,

this motor is not too common. It has a commutator at one end of the rotor. This is a rotating cluster of copper bars that are wired to winding circuits on the rotor. A pair of carbon brushes contact the commutator and complete the electrical circuit across the windings, first one, then the next and so on, as the rotor revolves. An electromagnetic field created by the rotor windings is positioned to repel the similar field created by the stator windings. These opposing forces produce very high twisting forces right from the start.

The repulsion principle would quickly shoot the motor speed beyond the desired running speed. For this reason centrifugal weights are positioned to fly outward and lift the brushes from the commutator. From that point on, the motor runs as a single-phase induction motor—hence the name, repulsion-induction.

SERIES MOTOR

Universal—one other type of motor you'll need to know about is the series motor, usually called a *universal* motor because it will run on either AC or DC. The stator and rotor windings are connected in series—that is, the current must flow first through one, then through the other. The rotating connection between the two is made with carbon brushes riding a commutator. In a universal motor the brushes do not lift from the

90

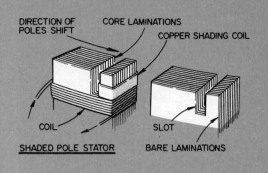

DIRECTION OF POLES SHIFT
CORE LAMINATIONS
COPPER SHADING COIL
COIL
SLOT
SHADED POLE STATOR
BARE LAMINATIONS

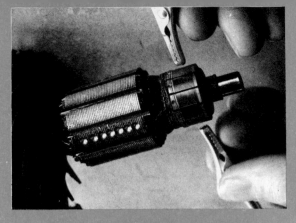

Test rotor for continuity by touching test probes on opposite sides of the commutator. There should be equal resistance all around.

commutator. If they did, the motor would stop.

Universal motors can run at speeds as high. as 35,000 revolutions per minute. Most run much slower.

High starting torque, high horsepower for their size and weight and the ability to adjust to widely varying loads and be speed controlled make universal motors ideal for drills, saws, shavers, sanders, blenders, vacuum cleaners and other portable household appliances. Their chief problems have to do with the brushes, which eventually wear down and have to be replaced. The commutator also can give problems, if dirty or pitted.

TROUBLESHOOTING

Finding the troubles of small motors is similar in all types. Just keep their differences in mind. Some have starting switches and squirrel cage rotors. Others have commutators, brushes and wire-wound rotors. Still others have none of these.

When a motor won't run, always check for the obvious. Is it plugged in? Is the fuse or circuit breaker okay?

Some motors are protected with thermostatically operated overload switches. If the motor overheats, the switch pops off. Some reset themselves when the windings cool off. Others must be reset by pushing a small red button when the motor cools. Check on this switch

before taking apart a motor that won't run.

Motors come apart without sweat. Usually two or four bolts hold the end bells together. Remove these and you can slip the ends off. Be sure to note whether there are any washers on the rotor shaft ends. These are spacers and should be replaced exactly as they come off.

MUST BE CLEAN

Inspect the contact points on the centrifugal switch to see that they are clean and making good electrical contact. If not, clean them with sandpaper. As a final step run a business card through them to clean off the residue left by sanding.

Often dirt and grease have fouled the operation of the centrifugal switch. The contacts should be closed when the motor is not running. They should open when the weight is moved outward from the rotor shaft. Clean the moving parts of the switch with solvent. Oil the parts very sparingly. Never over-lubricate a motor with a centrifugal switch. It leaks from the bearings and gums up the switch.

Sometimes too much end-play in the rotor shaft causes the centrifugal switch to malfunction. Additional fiber spacers may be needed between the shaft and

Worn brushes can be removed and replaced with new ones like this. Place curved side so that it conforms to commutator's angle.

Worn brushes can be removed and replaced with new ones like this. Place curved side so that it conforms to commutator's angle.

To clean dirty commutator back up fine sandpaper with object like a comb or stick. Run it over the spinning commutator.

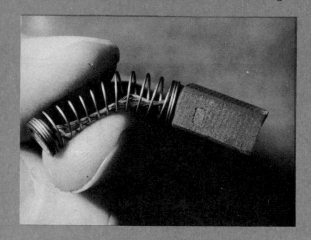

the end bell of the motor opposite the switch. Correct end-play is 0.005 to 0.030 inch.

TESTING

A VO meter is a great instrument for checking out a motor. Remove all the winding leads from the terminal strip. Tag them with tape so you can get them back the way they came off. The running windings are of heavier wire than the starting windings. Touch the leads of the test prods across pairs of leads for each winding. The ohm scale should show continuity of the wires. What's more, all the starting winding readings should be about the same. The running winding readings should all be about the same, too. A difference in readings signifies an open or short-circuited winding.

Make a ground test from the leads to the motor frame with the ohm selector set on the highest scale. Readings should show an open circuit (infinite ohms). If they don't, a winding is grounded. Replace it.

Rotor windings can be checked for continuity by touching the prods across

commutator bars on opposite sides of the shaft. If you find an open or shorted winding, replacement of the whole rotor or stator coil is called for. These can be rewound but buying a new motor can be cheaper. Motors usually are not very costly.

Likewise, test the rotor windings for grounding to the rotor shaft. There should be no continuity between the shaft and commutator bars. Replace the rotor if there is need to.

LET PRO DO IT

Testing a capacitor calls for a professional. Take it off and bring it to a shop for open, ground and capacitance tests. Handling a charged capacitor is dangerous. Discharge it through a light bulb before you touch the leads or handle it.

When a set of carbon brushes wears down, they should be replaced. Likewise, brushes should not hang up in their holders. They must make good contact with the commutator. Check the springs. Brushes are available in many sizes and shapes. If your electric motor parts dealer doesn't have what you want, you can

If mica insulators between commutator bars stick up, undercut with hacksaw blade. Edge-grind it first to remove all set from teeth.

To fit new brush, wrap strip of sandpaper around commutator and under brush, abrasive side out. Then turn rotor back and forth.

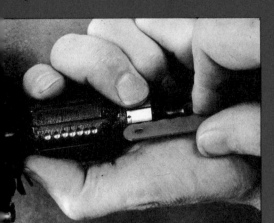

buy larger brushes and sandpaper them down to fit.

A dirty commutator can be cleaned by folding a piece of fine sandpaper over a flat stick and sliding it over the spinning commutator. Don't use emery paper or cloth. It carries current.

A badly scored commutator sometimes can be saved by turning it down on a lathe, then undercutting each strip of mica between copper bars with a hacksaw. If left high, the mica insulators would affect brush contact and cause arcing.

A split-phase or capacitor motor may be reversed easily if it turns the wrong way. Locate the two leads to the starting windings. One comes from the centrifugal switch. Switch these leads, one for another, and the motor will turn the other way. It's a trick not too many people know. It can come in handy at times.

Most motor problems are easy to find and fix. Use the troubleshooting chart given here. It covers most of the problems that small motors develop. Perhaps you can head off motor troubles by making inspection and lubrication right now.

INSULATION MATERIALS	
Wire Type	Insulation
S, SV SJ, SP	Rubber insulation for use in general purpose cords.
ST, SJT SVT, SPT	Thermoplastic PVC insulation for oil and water resistance and general use.
SO, SVO, SJO	Neoprene insulation for use in above normal heat conditions not exceeding 75°C. Excellent ozone and abrasion resistance.
SO-EZC SJO-EZC	Special insulation for resistance to ozone, heat vapors, water, oils, and lubricants. Highly flexible; excellent high and low temperature performance; good abrasion resistance, colorability; and color retention.
HPD	Cotton braid over neoprene insulated conductors for above-normal heat conditions and constant flexing.
HPN	Neoprene insulated paralleled conductors for use in above normal heat conditions not exceeding 90°C. Excellent ozone and abrasion resistance.

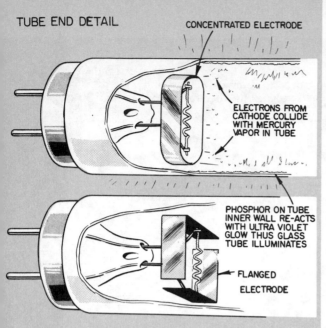

TUBE END DETAIL

CONCENTRATED ELECTRODE

ELECTRONS FROM CATHODE COLLIDE WITH MERCURY VAPOR IN TUBE

PHOSPHOR ON TUBE INNER WALL RE-ACTS WITH ULTRA VIOLET GLOW THUS GLASS TUBE ILLUMINATES

FLANGED ELECTRODE

FIXING FLUORESCENT LIGHTS

Troubleshooting begins with tube,

ballast and starter, in that order.

Fluorescent lights last a long time if they are burned continuously. And that's how you should use them. Believe it or not, you save money to leave a fluorescent light burning if you'll be needing it again in a short time. The lamps use very little current for the light they give. Starting them requires the action of a device called, what else, a *starter*. A fluorescent starter will take so

FLUORESCENT LIGHT TROUBLESHOOTING

Trouble	Cause	Cure
Flicker, swirl	Starter going out, wrong size or faulty ballast	Isolate the offender and replace.
	New tube	Should improve as tube ages.
Blinking	Too cold for lamp (below 50°F.)	Fluorescents are affected by cold drafts. Use protected fixtures or jacketed all-weather tubes. Also use starter and ballast designed for lowest temperature.
	Bum tube, faulty starter, loose contact, wrong or faulty ballast.	Isolate the offender and fix.
	Low circuit voltage	Correct
Hums	Normal ballast hum	Ignore it or replace with a low-noise ballast.
	Overheated or loose ballast	Check ballast temperature. Mount tightly.
End-of-tube blackening	Starter faulty or tube getting old	Replace starter or tube.
	Wrong or poor ballast connection	Check and correct.
Short tube life	Poor tube, too many starts, wrong or faulty ballast, faulty or wrong starter	Check ballasts' rated voltage and compare with house voltage. Replace with good ballast. Find other cause and correct.
	Loose or improper connection wrong circuit voltage.	Correct
Brownish rings about 2" from tube ends	Common but permissible	Don't worry.
Gray "feathers" on lower, cooler parts of tube.	Mercury not vaporized	Turn tube over to evaporate them.

many starts before it gives out. Then you have to buy a new one. Starting is hard on fluorescent tubes too. Turn them on and leave them on as long as you'll be needing the light.

Fluorescent tubes are filled with a current-carrying gas—mercury vapor. As the electricity passes through the gas, it glows, giving off ultraviolet light. Your eyes can barely see ultraviolet light, and so the addition of a coating inside the tube is necessary. This coating is called a *phosphor*. The phosphor glows brilliantly when exposed to ultraviolet radiation and the light it gives off is within the range that your eyes can see.

GETTING STARTED

To get the process started a pair of small filaments completely separated at the ends of the fluorescent tube begin to glow when you turn on the switch and the starter switches them into the circuit for a moment. The hot filaments vaporize droplets of mercury. As the starter automatically switches off the filaments, a voltage surge is applied across the ends of the tube. This gets electron flow started. The filaments are no longer incandescent. Instead, the AC power line is connected across the tube.

Once the merc vapor process gets going, the tube offers less and less resistance to current flow. It draws more and more current. The tube would eventually blow up were it not for a current-limiting device called a *ballast*. The ballast is a coil of fine wire that "chokes" back excessive current flow by electromagnetic induction. The ballast must be sized properly to hold the current at what the tube should receive.

Special "instant-start" tubes are made that don't need starters or preheating of filaments. They go when switched on. You can't use them unless your fluorescent fixture is designed to take them. There are also rapid-start preheat tubes. These can be used in a regular starter-type fixture.

Tube length governs how much light you get from a fluorescent. The kind of phosphor coating used determines the color of the light. Many colors are available.

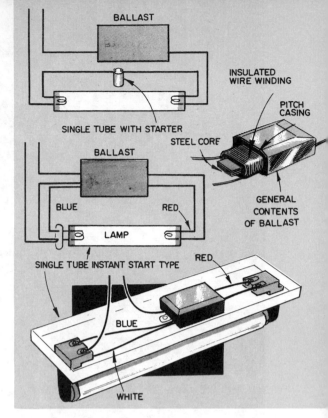

SINGLE TUBE WITH STARTER

BALLAST

BLUE RED

LAMP

SINGLE TUBE INSTANT START TYPE

INSULATED WIRE WINDING

PITCH CASING

STEEL CORE

GENERAL CONTENTS OF BALLAST

RED

BLUE

WHITE

PROBLEMS

The tube, the starter and the ballast are troublemakers, in that order. A starter is enclosed in a small can that fits into the chassis behind one of the tubes. A quarter-turn locks it in. In general you should replace the starter with every other tube replacement. The new starter must be the proper size for use with the tube.

Tubes darken on the ends with age. Their inner filaments can burn out and render them nonstarters. Never leave a nonstarting tube in a fixture. It overworks the starter and you'll soon need to replace that too. Check a tube for being tight in its socket. A quarter-turn after insertion does the job.

The only ballast check is to substitute another ballast known to be good, and of the right size. Some tube and starter switching among functioning and not functioning fluorescents of the same size can tell you. If the tube-starter combination work in one and not in the other, suspect the ballast.

This ceiling-hung fixture provides dramatic, effective lighting in key living room spots.

HOW TO PUT IN A
NEW LIGHT FIXTURE

Key factors are quantity, quality, color and reflectance of light

Your brightest ideas can result in glaring error if you leave light fixtures out of a home remodeling. Even if you're not planning a complete change of house decor, replacing an old ceiling fixture with a new one or installing new lighting in a capped ceiling outlet can work wonders for a room, suggests the American Home Lighting Institute.

In the '30s and '40s many harsh, glaring ceiling fixtures of the day were removed by homeowners looking for a better way. Their outlets were capped. Lamps were favored. New fixtures today are worthy additions to your home. See your electrical supplies dealer for a selection of what's available.

Fixtures are usually counted on to provide general illumination. When well chosen, they also add a decorative note and pleasant atmosphere. In selecting a fixture consider these basic principles of good lighting: Quantity, quality, color, and reflectance of light.

Individual fixtures may be combined with structural lighting for pleasing effects. See the chapter on adding outlets and lights for ideas on what you can do with structural lighting.

The fixture manufacturer's wattage rating and fixture size must be sufficient to handle the largest wattage lamps needed to light the room or the area around the fixture. Often, more than one fixture is required. For instance, a large kitchen may call for a pair of two-tube 48-inch fluorescent fixtures placed end to end.

WHAT TO LOOK FOR

Check your fixtures carefully before buying. Keep these points in mind:

•Incandescent lamps should not be closer than ¼ inch to enclosing globes or diffusion shields. Bare lamps should never be visible from the normal viewing angle.

•Top or side ventilation in a fixture is desirable to lower operating temperatures and will extend lamp life.

•The inside surface of shades should be of a polished material or white-enameled to reflect light.

•The fixture should be dimensioned and shaped to spread light efficiently and uniformly over the area you must light. The only way you can tell this is to see the fixture in action at your dealer's or try it in your home.

•The best material for enclosures and fixture shades is plain or textured glass or plastic.

•The fixtures in the drawing are de-

Starburst dining room ceiling fixture replaces old fixture in this lovely remodeled room.

signed to work well in the areas indicated. They're intended only as a guide. Many available fixture types are not shown. You may prefer a living room chandelier to any of the fixtures illustrated. Chandeliers are available with or without sparkle-type lamps that can be controlled by dimmer switches. Fluorescent fixtures with dimming ballasts can be controlled by dimmer switches, too. See the chapter on installing a light dimmer.

HOW TO INSTALL

The installation of a new light fixture is neither complicated nor dangerous. You'll need a ladder to reach the fixture. Never work from a stool or chair. That's dangerous.

All necessary parts and hardware are

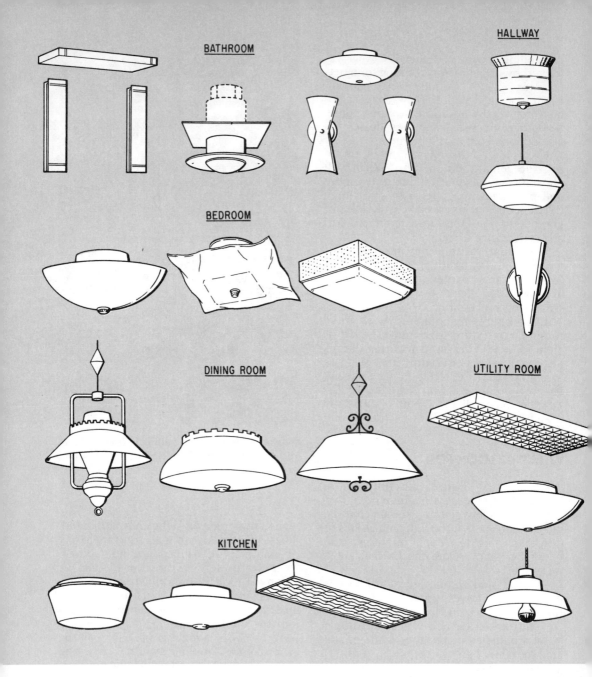

BATHROOM

HALLWAY

BEDROOM

DINING ROOM

UTILITY ROOM

KITCHEN

usually supplied with the new fixture, along with step-by-step installation instructions for it. Check your electrical code before you begin. As with other electrical work, fixture installation in some areas may require a licensed electrician.

The first step is to turn off current to the fixture. Merely having the wall switch off isn't enough. Someone may acciden-

tally turn it on just as you have the black and white wires in your hands. You'll utter something like "Yow!" After that your remarks are likely to be unprintable. So be sure to throw the circuit breaker to *off* or remove the fuse protecting that circuit. If you can't find the right fuse, throw the main switch at the fuse panel or remove the main disconnect, whichever type you have.

The next step is to remove the canopy covering the old fixture's mounting and clip off the two fixture wires. Remove the fixture from its mounting. Most old-style fixtures are screwed to a threaded stud in the center of the ceiling box. Others are fastened to metal straps, which are in turn fastened to the box with screws. They can be removed by loosening the screws that hold the fixture to the strap.

First remove old fixture, taking off nuts or screws holding it to fixture box. Turn off current, unfasten wires to old fixture.

MOUNTING NEW FIXTURE

If the old fixture strap is the same size as the new one, don't change it. Otherwise, mount the new fixture strap and attach the fixture to the strap with the screws or bolts that come with it. You are now ready to make up the wiring connections.

It often helps to fashion a temporary fixture hanger from a wire clothes hanger. Hook it to the fixture box and fixture, so it supports the fixture while you work on the wiring.

Expose both the house and fixture wire ends by stripping the insulation down to bare, clean copper wire. One wire of each should be black, the other white. Match the black fixture wire to the black house wire and twist the bared ends together. Screw a solderless connector over them.

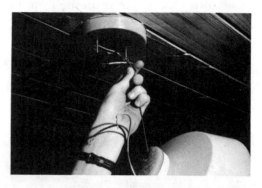

Hang the new fixture in position with a hook made from a length of coat hanger wire. The hook end should rest right on fixture box.

Match the white wires and splice them with a solderless connector. If both fixture wires are the same color, be sure to connect the black house wire with the fixture wire coming from the center terminal of the socket. This leaves the threaded socket portion neutral.

Push the connected wires as close as possible around the fixture mounting, making sure that the wires don't rub against any surface that might wear through the insulation and bare the conductors.

Finally, cover the mounting with the new canopy. Install the necessary bulbs and the diffusing bowl or glass, if any. Then replace the removed fuse or switch on the *off* breaker.

To keep light fixtures working brightly, give them periodic cleaning. Four to six times a year is the recommended interval.

Splice the black fixture wire to the black box wire and white to white. Use solderless connectors if your code okays them. Then mount the new fixture to box, taking care to get wires tucked neatly away in the box.

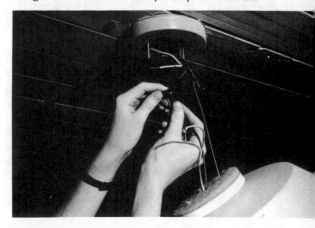

YOUR OWN POWER AT HOME OR AWAY

Small portable electric plant is handy for camping or an emergency

You never realize just how valuable electric power is until it goes out during a storm. The answer is to have your own electric power in the form of a small portable electric plant to provide power when and where you need it. An electric plant that's portable is handy for boating or camping, too. You can take along an electric skillet and a portable TV. Watch the ball game while dinner cooks. Take a light along, too, even your electric blanket.

For full use of a vacation home beyond power lines, you'd want a larger sized electric plant, permanently installed, not portable.

The handiest electric plants operate with gasoline engines. The engine spins an alternator, which produces electricty. Just plug into the handy receptacles on the unit. Fuel used is proportional to the load, except at idle. You can use 1000 watts for 3.3 hours on one gallon, approximately.

Many electric plants give three-wire single-phase power in 120 and 240 volts and 60-cycle AC. That's the same as what your utility likely furnishes. The difference is that you'd need a whale of an electric plant to produce all the electricity used in your home. It wouldn't be practical to have such a large unit merely for standby use during a power failure. And the power plant would be much too big to carry along on a camping trip or picnic.

What size unit then? It all depends on what you'll use it for. If standby power is what you want, figure the bare minimum power needed during a power failure. For comfort you'll want the heating plant to run, if it isn't electric heat. It would be nice to have some light, say

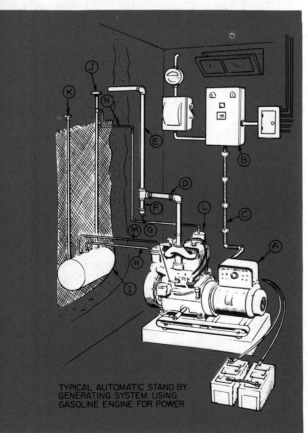

TYPICAL AUTOMATIC STAND BY GENERATING SYSTEM USING GASOLINE ENGINE FOR POWER

A. Remote starting engine-generator; B. automatic emergency transfer control; C. Greenfield circuit; D. flexible exhaust tubing; E. exhaust stack to muffler; F. condensation trap; G. drain cock; H. fuel line; I. underground fuel tank; J. vent caps—underground tank; K. locking fill cap — underground tank; L. reservoir tank (1 quart); M. return line (overflow); N. vent line.

POWER REQUIREMENTS OF ELECTRIC MOTORS

Motor H.P. Rating	WATTS REQUIRED TO START			
	Approx. "running" Watts	Split-Phase Motors	Capacitor-Start Motors	Repulsion-Induction Motors
1/6	275	2050	850	600
1/4	400	2400	1050	850
1/3	450	2700	1350	975
1/2	600	3600	1800	1300
3/4	850	....	2600	1900
1	1100	....	3300	2500

several living room lamps. And you'd want power to run a sump pump to keep the basement dry. This could well be the total of your "get-by" power needs. Figure how much wattage is needed to power these necessities. Always figure for maximum load, because that's what your electric plant will have to contend with. You can stagger the use of equipment to reduce maximum load. For instance, turn off the heating plant while you run the sump pump. Then you need figure only the wattage used by the heaviest of these.

When it comes to motors, you need more wattage to get them started than to run them under load. Allow three to four times the running wattage of a split-phase motor for its starting wattage. Allow one-and-one-half times on capacitor motors. These have "lumps" on the sides with the capacitors in them. Figuring for more than one motor, use the starting wattage of the largest and the running wattage of the others.

Your maximum standby power requirements probably come to something like 3000 watts. Most of the load is motor starting load. You could get by with a much smaller engine-generator set if it weren't for that. Once the sump pump and other motors were running, you could turn on quite a few more lights, or even use a toaster on the vast reserve power.

A 1500-watt unit is a nice size for carrying around in the trunk of the car. It can be used to run a saw, electric drill or other power tools while building a vacation cabin in the woods. An electric

plant that will supply the "running" current for a power tool will also handle starting it up. The reason is that power tools can be started while not under a load. They can reach full speed before applying the load.

A permanent hookup of an electric plant is done through a transfer switch. This a double-pole double-throw switch that disconnects utility power lines and connects your standby power once the generator is running at full speed. You can even get transfer switches that work automatically when power fails. Never hook a standby power plant into your house wiring without using an approved transfer switch.

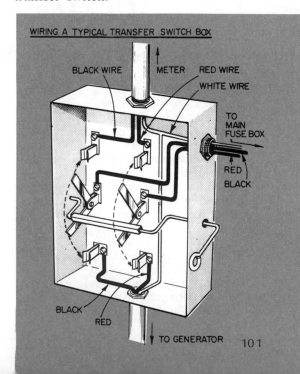

WIRING A TYPICAL TRANSFER SWITCH BOX

BLACK WIRE — METER — RED WIRE — WHITE WIRE — TO MAIN FUSE BOX — RED — BLACK — BLACK — RED — TO GENERATOR

Pilot and burner controls on a gas clothes dryer are complex. Sometimes pilot-starter filament is broken. Check its glow at cycle's start. If control's the trouble, replace.

BASIC GUIDE TO MAJOR
APPLIANCE REPAIR

Master relay controls and these'll be easier than small appliances

Electrical troubles in major home appliances are sometimes easier to diagnose and repair than troubles in small appliances. The wiring systems in some are simple; in others, complex. Take-apart is seldom much of a problem as it is in the small appliances.

As with small appliances, the big ones can develop mechanical troubles as well as electrical ones. We'll concentrate on the electricity. That's enough for a first step.

Major appliances make use of several electrical controls that may be new to you. One is the relay. Previously mentioned in connection with electric heating, a relay is an electrically operated remote switch that permits one flow of current to control another current. Your car's horns honk, not when you press the horn control, but when the horn control tells a relay to send electricity to the horns. It all works so quickly that the action seems instantaneous. Relays perform many functions in circuitry. One is to act as a simple contactor. The purpose in this case is to let a small current flow control a larger one.

BAR BECOMES
AN ELECTROMAGNET

Relays work electromagnetically. The light-duty horn control current flows through coils of wire around a soft iron bar. The coil and bar becomes an electromagnet. The magnetism attracts a movable metal arm containing a contact. This contact closes on another contact and the circuit is completed to the car's horns.

Relays used on washing machines and dryers work the same way. They're remote, heavy-current switches controlled by light currents. "Open" coils and dirty or welded-closed relay contacts, among other things, render them inoperative. Continuity tests can be performed on the primary coil circuit and on the relay contact circuit. Both should have continuity. If you can't quickly cure a sick relay, remove it and get another. Be sure to tag all wires for proper reassembly.

In appliance circuits it is not unusual to find a relay switching the neutral side of the 120-volt line. Thus one of the contacts would be at ground potential. Don't let that throw you. Also in a 120-volt relay, one end of the relay's coil wire may be at ground potential.

SOLENOIDS

Another device used widely in heavy appliances is the solenoid. A solenoid converts electricity into a push or a pull through electromagnetic action. Coils of wire are wrapped around a soft iron bar. The bar is loose, free to move in and out. When current flows through the coils, magnetism created pulls the bar forcefully into the coil. The gear shift lever, drive belt idler pulley, water valve

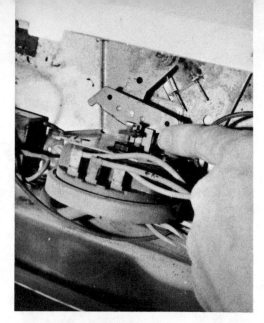

This automatic washer's low-water valve reacts to air pressure created by water rising in a plastic tube. A switch closes fill valve when desired water level is reached.

or whatever is attached is pulled along with the bar. Later, after the current has been released, a spring or another opposing solenoid pulls the coil out again, reversing the action.

A special solenoid fill valve is used to control water coming into a washer or dishwasher. It ingeniously combines a small needle-pointed solenoid valve to control a full flow of water under pressure (see drawing).

Like relays, solenoids may be checked for continuity, though, a nonfunctioning solenoid is more likely to be the fault of binding mechanical parts than trouble

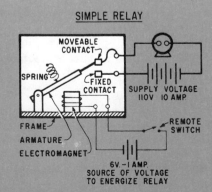

HOW A SOLENOID WORKS

120 VOLTS
COIL
SPRING PULLS BAR BACK WHEN CURRENT FLOW IS STOPPED
MAGNETISM PULLS BAR INTO COIL OF WIRE
IRON BAR

SIMPLE RELAY

MOVEABLE CONTACT
SPRING
FIXED CONTACT
FRAME
ARMATURE
ELECTROMAGNET
SUPPLY VOLTAGE 110V 10 AMP
REMOTE SWITCH
6V.-1 AMP. SOURCE OF VOLTAGE TO ENERGIZE RELAY

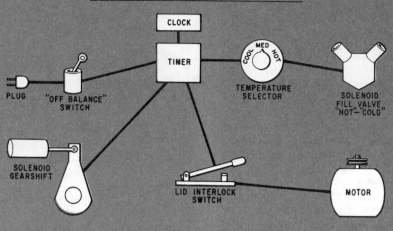

Large appliances are easier to open than small ones. Top of automatic washer lifts like hood of an auto to expose top working parts. Reach other parts from back, bottom.

The VO meter is used for making continuity checks of the programmer and the timer of this automatic washer. All of the wires are color-coded to help in troubleshooting.

with the solenoid. Sometimes a little lubrication or adjustment to the mechanism works wonders.

TIMERS

The master control of automatic washers, clothes dryers and dishwashers is the timer. It tells the machine what to do and when to do it. For each control

circuit in the machine there is a pair of small timer contacts. These are opened and closed when needed by a cam. The cam is moved by a clock-like timer mechanism that rotates it a notch every so often. This is better than a steady rotation because it closes and opens contacts quickly. That prevents burning. If many circuits are to be controlled — an automatic washer can have ten or more —

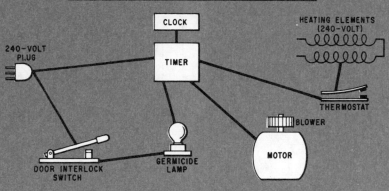

SCHEMATIC OF AUTOMATIC CLOTHES DRYER CIRCUITS

CLOCK

HEATING ELEMENTS
(240-VOLT)

240-VOLT
PLUG

TIMER

THERMOSTAT

DOOR INTERLOCK
SWITCH

GERMICIDE
LAMP

BLOWER

MOTOR

many cams will be clustered on a drum. Many contacts ride the cams, each dancing to its own tune.

One movable contact is sometimes placed between two stationary ones. Pushed one way by the cam, it opens the first circuit and closes another.

When contacts close, solenoids are energized, belts tightened, valves opened, gears shifted and motors started. The most probable timer trouble is dirty contacts. If one set of contacts fails to close its circuits, or welds shut and fails to open its circuit, the symptoms can show up in many ways. It all depends on which contacts are affected. In troubleshooting you have to know what is supposed to happen but doesn't. Then you can trace the wiring back to the faulty contacts. Cleaning with fine folded sandpaper usually gets things working again. Sometimes replacement of the timer is called for.

AUTOMATIC WASHERS

Many types of automatic washers are made. All have a motor, drive belt, gears, water pump, timer and cabinet. Some have an agitator, others have a pulsator.

When the timer is started its motor takes charge of it throughout the rest of the cycle. By opening and closing con-

tacts, the timer makes the washer fill, wash, spin-empty, fill again, rinse, spin-empty, fill again and spin-dry. Washer cycles vary among makes but are similar. Temperature control is usually by a dual solenoid valve. One side is used for cold, another for hot. This valve is controlled through some fill cycles by a temperature selector switch. Other fill cycles bypass the selector switch.

Some washers have automatic programmers that vary the cycle according to which fabric selector buttons have been pressed. These controls are complex, electrically as well as mechanically.

When something goes wrong with your washer, get out the VO meter or test light, swing open the top or side access to the cabinet and isolate the trouble. Then fix it. Don't be discouraged if the problem eludes you and the repairman has to be called. He spent weeks in school learning how to meet washer problems head on. You may have to back away from some of them.

CLOTHES DRYER

Dryers use gas or electricity to heat air that is blown through your tumbling clothes. All have drums, heaters, motors

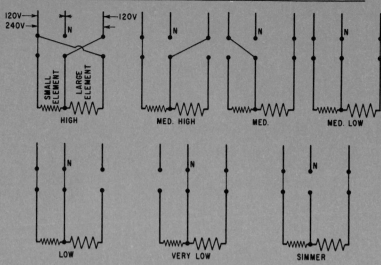

120V→
240V→
←120V

SMALL ELEMENT LARGE ELEMENT

HIGH   MED. HIGH   MED.   MED. LOW

LOW   VERY LOW   SIMMER

If solenoid-operated fill valve won't let water through, remove terminals to see if there's power to them during "fill" cycle.

Heating element at dishwasher tub bottom won't heat if there's no power. Check it. Interlock should be closed, cycle on "dry."

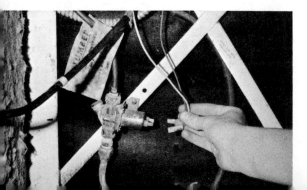

and blowers. Thermostats and timers control these parts. The dryer mechanism is enclosed in a cabinet. An interlock switch stops all dryer operation when the access door is opened.

Gas dryers have glow-elements that start the pilot flame. This does away with the need for a continous pilot. The pilot is turned out at the end of the cycle by the timer.

Electric dryers have no need of a pilot control. The 240-volt heating element turns on and off as needed to maintain proper drying temperatures. The split-phase dryer motor runs on 120 volts, half of the 240-volt 3-wire line brought to an electric dryer.

About five minutes before the end of the cycle the heater shuts off to let the clothes and tumbler drum cool before the drum stops.

Most dryer troubles can be traced to motor, timer, circuit continuity or mechanical malfunctions. A dryer's timer is similar to a washer's timer but simpler. Use your VO meter or test light to check the circuits that don't seem to work as they should. Be especially careful of the 240 volts in an electric dryer.

ELECTRIC RANGE

Modern electric ranges may seem like

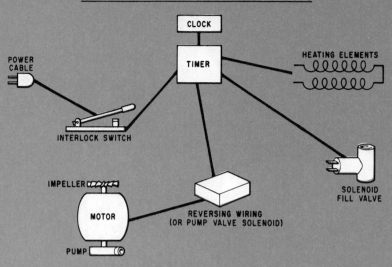

complicated combinations of switches, heating elements, timers, pilot lamps and thermostats, but the circuits are simple. Each surface cooking unit is controlled by a switch. By an ingenious switching of 120-volt and 240-volt three-wire power between an inner and an outer heating element, seven heats can be had. *High*—both elements are hooked in parallel on 240; *medium high*—smaller element on 240; *medium*—larger element on 240; *medium low*—both elements in parallel on 120; *low*—smaller element on 120; *very low*—larger element on 120; and *simmer*—both elements in series on 240. Some ranges feature three-heat switching. Ranges all operate on 120/240 volt three-wire service.

Oven units have two heating elements placed one above and one below the unit. Three or four heats are available in ovens. Timers are interconnected for on-off control without you being on hand. Ovens use thermostats to control temperatures. When the thermostat says it's hot enough, it switches off the heating element. Some surface units have thermostatic control too.

Electric ranges have few moving parts and give little trouble. Bad-acting thermostats top the list. Once in a while a silver switch contact fouls up. Get a circuit diagram for the range and check continuity with a VO meter and test light. Watch out for the 240.

DISHWASHER

Dishwasher components are much like those of an automatic washer, but much simpler. A timer controls the washing cycle. A fill valve lets hot water in for a power rinse. The motor spins backward to pump the rinse water out into an air-gap drain. The fill valve opens again, filling the tub with hot water. A soap container mechanically dumps and the impeller spins to begin the wash cycle. Pump-out, fill, rinse, and pump-out complete the power portion of the cycle. Then a heating element is energized to dry the load. When it switches off, the cycle ends. An interlock switch cuts all power while the dishwasher is opened. If nothing will work, check its operation.

Continuity checks will diagnose most electrical troubles of dishwashers. Mechanical problems are few. A mineral-clogged diaphragm in the fill valve is a major problem in iron water areas. Timer contacts can go sour. Heating elements can burn out. Wires can vibrate against metal parts and short. Check for these troubles first.

107

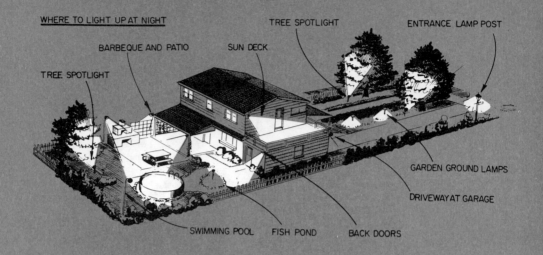

WHERE TO LIGHT UP AT NIGHT

TREE SPOTLIGHT

ENTRANCE LAMP POST

BARBEQUE AND PATIO

SUN DECK

TREE SPOTLIGHT

GARDEN GROUND LAMPS

DRIVEWAY AT GARAGE

SWIMMING POOL   FISH POND   BACK DOORS

Drawing, adapted from General Electric, shows recommended placement of outdoor lights.

RIGHT WAYS TO USE
OUTDOOR WIRING

At stake is convenience, safety, recreation, beauty and security

Outdoor wiring does the same thing for your outdoors that indoor wiring does for your indoors. Extending electricity to the out-of-doors offers convenience, safety, recreation, beauty and security to your house and grounds.

Outdoor wiring can make your porch or patio a multi-purpose extension of the living area. Further wiring can create a backdrop of light and color on trees and shrubs. Outdoor lighting can set a mood for your home. It can extend a warm welcome to arriving guests long before you greet them at the door. Light is security,

too. It's comforting to know that there is a ring of light around your home whether the lights are turned on or not.

OUTDOOR SYSTEMS

There are two types of outdoor lighting systems: 120-volt and low-voltage. Low-voltage systems operate on 6 or 12 volts. You can choose either type if your code permits. Here's how the two stack up: The 120-volt system has it all over the lower voltage for pushing large amounts of electricity through long runs of wiring. Also, 120-volt juice is required for outdoor outlets to operate power tools, electric grills and the like. On the other hand, low-voltage systems are far safer. If a wire should be bared, you couldn't get hurt by the 12 volts it carries, even if you touched the bare wire with hands and wet feet.

The most sensible way to handle outdoor wiring seems to be to use 120-volt wiring for all permanent outdoor receptacles and fixtures. This includes those attached to the house. They can be wired as additional outlets directly from the house wiring circuits. The method is described in the chapter on adding outlets and lights.

Other permanently wired fixtures needed are lights and receptacles on barbecue grills, post lights and yard outlets for the use of power tools and pumps for fountains. Most outdoor permanent light-ing calls for 150-watt lamps. For example, an outdoor barbecue grill and picnic table should have at least two 150-watt lights preferably in different locations 12 to 20 feet above the ground in trees or on poles. Telescoping poles are available for such use.

The low-voltage system is best used for small temporary or movable lights around the yard. These lights can be fastened to walls or fences, staked in the ground or hung in trees. They serve as lighting for the house, garden, patio, walks, pools, ponds, planters, eating areas, steps or anywhere else you need smaller spots of light. They're very easy to wire up.

120-VOLT WIRING

Outdoor wiring in 120-volts must be as carefully installed as indoor wiring. Use Type UF cable. Outdoor 120-volt

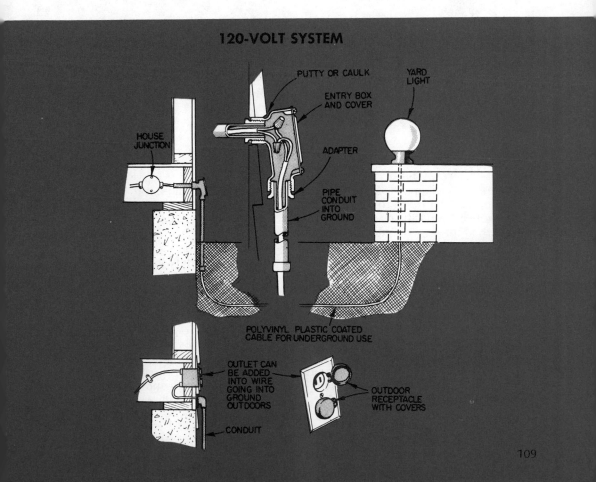

120-VOLT SYSTEM

LOW-VOLTAGE SYSTEM

WIRING PERMANENT OUTLETS

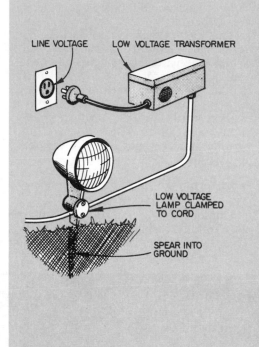

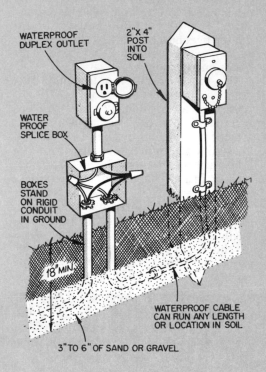

circuits can originate at the entrance panel or can be taken off some other fused house circuit. If the outdoor circuit is switched inside, you may use a normal switch. Outside switches should be the weatherproof type. All cables should contain a third grounding wire in addition to the black and white wires. Outlets must be the three-prong grounding type. Wire them into weatherproof boxes and covers. Most weatherproof outlet covers have hinged or screw-on caps to keep water out when not in use. Cords should be removed from the outlets when unattended, or else the space between the plug and the outlet should be taped.

Ideally, 120-volt cable should be buried in a trench at least 18 inches below ground. Lay a creosoted board or a row of bricks over the cable before you backfill to keep someone from accidentally cutting into the cable while digging. In an area where no one will dig, you can bury the cable several inches below ground. Be sure to cover with boards or bricks for positive protection.

Type UF cable must not be exposed at any point outdoors. Where cable enters and comes out of the ground it must be in rigid conduit. Weatherproof boxes are threaded for direct installation on the threaded conduit ends. Leave some slack in the cable at each end of a run to allow for shrinkage when cold.

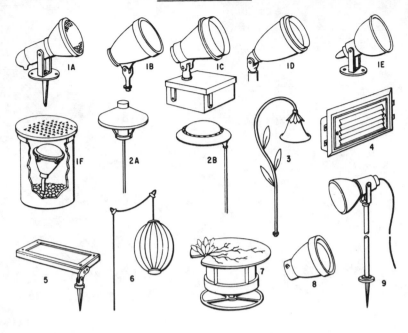

OUTDOOR FIXTURES: 1) adjustable holders; a) reflector lamps; b) with deep metal shielding; c) mercury vapor floods; d) with cover lens; e) enclosed floodlight for regular bulbs; 2) mushroom unit; 3) bell-type reflector; 4) recessed walkway light; 5) weatherproof fluorescent; 6) diffusing plastic shade light; 7) underwater pond light; 8) underwater flood; 9) telescopic enclosed pole light.

Outside switches and receptacle boxes may be attached to the house, to trees, to a fence post or a freestanding post. They also may stand free from rigid conduit coming out of the ground.

HOW TO AVOID SHOCK

When you use outdoor receptacles the normal precautions to avoid shock can be lifesavers. Use only grounded or double-insulated portable power tools outdoors. Stand on dry ground. Lay planks if necessary. Don't plug in any 120-volt appliance near a swimming pool, whether the pool is above-ground or in-ground. If a plugged-in appliance should be knocked into the pool, swimmers could be electrocuted. It happens every year. Neither should swimmers touch appliances with wet hands or bare feet. Use battery-operated portable radios at poolside.

Pool lights can be dangerous too. It's best to use low-voltage lights and have a professional wire them, even to an above-ground pool. A 120-volt pool light, even though it's grounded, can charge the pool water with electricity. Underwater wiring is nothing for us do-it-ourselfers to attempt.

Do not use indoor cords outdoors. All extension cords for power tools, Christmas trees, and other uses should be of the types recommended for outdoor use. This includes types S, SJ, ST and SJT.

Skillful use of outdoor lights can open up the exterior of your house after dark for outdoor living and safety. The eave lights above are wired and switched from inside the home.

Use the kind with molded-on plugs and taps. If you make up your own, put plastic electrical tape around the joint between the plug and cord and between the tap and cord to keep out water. Never splice or repair an outdoor cord. Replace it.

Lamps used outdoors where rain can hit them should not be more than 25 watters. Otherwise they can break.

LOW-VOLTAGE LIGHTING

Low-voltage outdoor systems are obviously useful only for lighting. You'd need a whole new set of power tools to use in low-voltage receptacles. Low-voltage outdoor lighting usually comes in kits of varying sizes. Included are a transformer to step down the 120-volt house current to 6 or 12 volts, wires, connectors and lights. Transformer sizes to 300 watts are available. The amount of light per circuit is somewhat limited, the average lamp size being only 15-watt. The lights should be placed close to what they are to illuminate. Wires, connectors, fixtures, lamps and mounting stakes are included too.

Some low-voltage lighting kits use resealing cables to which the lampholders are clamped. Pointed prongs pierce the cable and contact the conductors. Some Christmas tree lights work this way. But in the outdoor version when the lampholder is removed, the cable reseals the

GROUND FAULT SENTRY CONCEPT

PANEL BOARD

HOT

NEUTRAL

ISOLATION TRANSFORMER

LOAD

SENSING CIRCUIT

Ground fault sentry is an outdoor wiring device that protects against the hazards of current leakage to ground. Isolating transformer leaves no direct path for fault current to follow back to supply. Sensing circuit cuts off circuit immediately if slightest fault is detected. This system is excellent for pool lighting and other electricity around water.

openings. Low-voltage wiring may go to 100 feet without serious voltage drop. It's a good idea to tape low-voltage connections after assembling to make them waterproof.

All wiring from the house circuit to the low-voltage transformer must be installed to National Electric Code standards. From that point on, the voltage wiring can be handled more casually under most codes. Low-voltage wires may be run on top of the ground if they're placed where no one can trip on them. If you string low-voltage wires overhead, they should be high enough so people won't run into them. The transformer itself should be designed with overload protection as a safeguard against overheating.

MERCURY VAPOR LIGHT

In many areas utility companies will rent you an automatically switched mer-

cury vapor pole light that can light a 60- to 100-foot circle. Most farms have them. The cost to operate one is small. Because many people object to the bluish color of the light, filtered models are often available.

Electric eye device can be wired to turn lights on at dark, off at dawn. It wires into ordinary switchbox on outside wall, but where eye can't "see" lights being controlled.

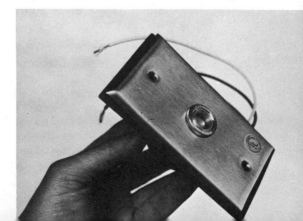

INSTALL A LIGHT DIMMER

Go from full bright to candlelight

—and save money at the same time

A modern light dimmer is easy to install and it provides full light control, along with extended lamp life and lowered bills.

If you can install a light switch, you can put in a light dimmer. You benefit in several ways. First is the lighting control it makes possible. As one dimmer manufacturer puts it, you have "any light from full bright to candlelight." Moreover, a dimmer saves you money. You pay only for the wattage used. A 150-watt lamp dimmed half way actually uses less than 75 watts of power. And the dimmer takes less than half a watt for itself. You also benefit in longer lamp life. A voltage cut of only 10 percent makes a lamp last four times its normal life. Operated at half voltage, a bulb is as permanent as the fixture it's in. At a candle glow you'd get a century of service from one bulb.

You will find a light dimmer useful for controlling living room lights, dining room fixture, a TV viewing light, a pole lamp, and a bedroom ceiling fixture. Hall lights, when dimmed, make great night lights. Every house can use several dimmers.

TYPES AVAILABLE

You can buy several different kinds of light dimmers. The size should be sufficient to handle all the lights controlled by it. Sizes can be had from 200-watt to as big as you could want.

Some dimmers work electronically. Unless protected against overloads, this kind may not be used to control a lamp that is plugged into an outlet. The dimmer could be overloaded dangerously by plugging a waffle iron, for instance, into the outlet.

Full-range knob-controlled dimmers are top-of-the-line controls. Some are simple, electronically operated replacements for switches. They fit the same box and new wiring unless both white and black wires are available at the switch. The transformer types have an advantage or two. They can't cause radio TV interference, as the electronic dimmers sometimes do. They're also hardier in surviving overcurrents caused by storms.

ANY LEVEL POSSIBLE

Turning the knob of either type brings the light level up from full *off* to full *on* in a smooth progression. You may stop at any level you like. You can get a three-way version for replacing one switch where two stitches control a light. A dimmer cannot be installed on both the switches — just one.

To prevent radio interference from an electronic dimmer, keep the dimmer power lines at least six feet from the power lines to a radio.

Some knob-controlled half-range dimmers give smooth control only half way up, then jump to full *on*. They sell a little cheaper than the full-range jobs.

You can get a two-step dimmer switch that replaces an ordinary light switch to permit full *on*, half dimmed, and *off*. *Dim* is in the center of the switch's three positions so you can light a child's room without waking him.

The simplest dimmer is called a bulb-extender. It is merely an *on-off* switch that gives either no light or dimmed light. It's good for switching fixtures with hard-to-replace bulbs or for night lights. A better bet for the replacement problem is a long-life lamp.

INSTALLATION

Turn off the circuit at the entrance panel and take the old switch out. Then connect the switch wires to the dimmer. Mount the dimmer in the switch box, install the cover plate — a special one may be furnished — and you're done. Turn on the power again and you have light control.

Special dimmers are made for use with fluorescent lights. They call for the installation of a special dimming ballast inside the fixture enclosure. A three-wire cable is needed from the dimmer to the fixture. Plan to replace the existing cable when you install the dimmer. A fluorescent dimmer costs about twice what one for dimming an incandescent light does, but your fluorescents needn't be without brightness control.

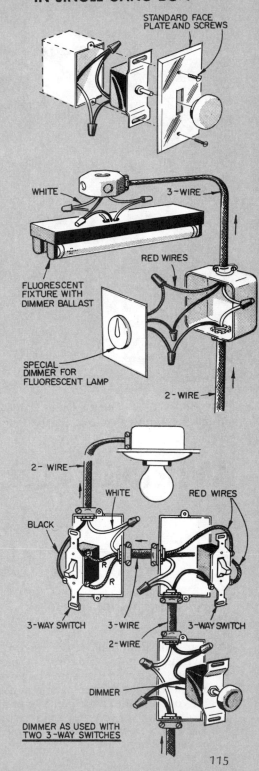

TYPICAL DIMMER INSTALLATION IN SINGLE GANG BOX

STANDARD FACE PLATE AND SCREWS

WHITE

3 - WIRE

RED WIRES

FLUORESCENT FIXTURE WITH DIMMER BALLAST

SPECIAL DIMMER FOR FLUORESCENT LAMP

2 - WIRE

2 - WIRE

WHITE

RED WIRES

BLACK

R

R

3-WAY SWITCH

3 - WIRE

3-WAY SWITCH

2 - WIRE

DIMMER

DIMMER AS USED WITH TWO 3-WAY SWITCHES

Whether you're building a home addition or a vacation retreat, the proper procedure is to install the wiring after you get the framing completed and the sides and roof closed in.

WIRING YOUR HOME ADDITION OR VACATION HOUSE

New-work wiring is easier than old, but plan your circuits carefully

You will find that putting electrical wiring in new structures is much easier and more fun than threading wires through the hidden spaces of old houses. When you add onto your home or put up a vacation house, you may enjoy wiring it yourself. New-work wiring goes pleasingly fast. There are few problems, if any.

Plan the circuits for your new structure carefully. There should be enough circuits to fill all its electrical needs. Follow NEC recommendations and provide a 15-amp general-purpose circuit for each 375 square feet of living space or a 20-amp circuit for each 500 square feet. For instance, if an attic addition contains 800 square feet of living space, you'd want to furnish three 15-amp circuits or two 20-amp circuits to its lights and outlets (see table).

As a double check add up the wattage you'll be using on each circuit, present and future, as near as you can estimate. A 15-amp circuit will handle 1725 watts (15 amps×115 volts=1725 watts). A 20-amp circuit will handle 2300 watts (20 amps×115 volts=2300 watts). A motor-serving circuit is different. It can qualify for only 80 percent of the normal rating. Thus, instead of 1725 watts, a 15-amp circuit can handle only 1380 watts with motors. A 20-amp circuit can serve only 1840 watts with motors.

DON'T OVERLOAD

Whether your entrance wiring can take an additional load depends on its maximum capacity and how much of this is being used.

First find the capacity. Sometimes it's shown on the service panel: 30, 60, 100 are common ampere ratings. If you can find the size of wires that lead into the service panel from the meter, you can look up their current-carrying capacity in the table in the chapter on how your house is wired. If the cylindrical cartridge fuses behind the main disconnect in your service panel have been sized to make full use of the entrance wiring, they will tell you what power is available.

Suppose you find 100-ampere service. The next step is to see how much of that 100 amperes is being used. If you can figure your income tax, you can figure electrical load. Don't simply add up the amperage of all your fuses or circuit breakers. This would have meaning only if every appliance were operating at the same time. Instead, figure the percentage of watts that are likely to be used at one time. You can figure kitchen circuits at 1500 watts each because kitchen appliances aren't used all at one time on both circuits. Laundry area, too. General purpose lighting appliance circuits are figured at 3 watts per square foot of living space.

Service or branch panel is wired from the top with three heavy gauge wires coming from meter or existing panel. Choose their size according to load they have to serve.

| NO. OF CIRCUITS | FLOOR SPACE SERVED | |
	15-AMP	20-AMP
1	375	500
2	750	1000
3	1125	1500
4	1500	2000
5	1875	2500
6	2250	3000
7	2625	3500

RECOMMENDED GENERAL PURPOSE CIRCUITS

ENTRANCE WIRE CAPACITY
(3% voltage drop, 75-foot or less run)

Gauge	Overhead Copper*	Overhead Aluminum*	Buried Copper Type RHW
14			15
12			20
10	50	45	30
8	70	50	45
6	1000	80	60
4	130	100	80
3			100
2	175	130	115
1	200	150	130
0		175	150
2/0		200	175
3/0			200

*Overhead spans must be at least No. 10 for spans to 50 feet, No. 8 for longer spans.

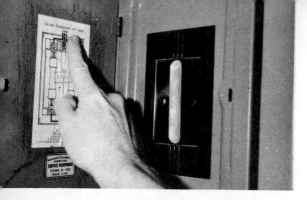

To tell whether your house has the electrical guts for additional load, read rating on service panel. It usually appears on outside.

Underground entrance wires come down utility pole in conduit: metallic at bottom, non-metallic at top: conduit's below ground.

RHW lead-in wires are uncoiled and buried at least 18" below ground in trench, protecting them from lightning, falling trees.

SAMPLE CALCULATION

What's more, the National Code lets you omit the wattage of either air conditioner or heating system if you have both. The reason is that both will not likely be working at once. Omit the smaller power-user of the two.

Then only the first 10,000 watts of power is figured at 100 percent. That over 10,000 watts may be figured at 40 percent of full value. Here's how a sample load calculation might look:

	Watts
Living area of house (__ sq. feet) times 3 =	___
Two kitchen appliance circuits	3000
Laundry circuit	1500
Workshop appliance circuit	1500
Range, water heater	___
Space heating	___
Other large permanently connected appliances	___
Total wattage	___

If the total wattage is more than 10,000 —say 31,500—add to 10,000 40 percent of the excess over 10,000 (40/100ths × 21,500 = 8600) (10,000 + 8600 = 18,600 watts total load.)

When you know your house electrical capacity and load, compare the two figures to see whether the additional will put you in hot water electrically. If it won't, go ahead and wire the new circuit from the existing service panel. If you have a total load of 18,600 watts with 100-ampere service, you're in good shape. Why? Because 100 amperes times 230 volts gives a power capacity of 23,000 watts; 18,600 watts is well under. If you had only 60-ampere service, you'd be in trouble. It gives only 13,800 available watts—and would aready be far overloaded at the 18,600-watt loading.

Along with your home addition you may need to modernize your service entrance to take a bigger load, plus future load. If the calculations throw you, ask your power company rep to figure the load for you.

VACATION HOME LOAD

Figuring the electrical load on a vacation home is not much different. If you plan it for full leisure time living, equip it electrically just as you would your home. But since it will likely be much smaller than your home, it will not need as large a service entrance. On the other hand, some vacation houses are located where the only utility available is electricity. In that case, you'll want to do everything with electricity: cooking, water heating and possibly heating the house, too. The service entrance should be matched to the load.

When you've calculated the total load and reduced the amount over 10,000 watts by 40 percent, divide by the voltage to get the service panel you need.

Suppose, for example, that your total load figured up like this:

	Watts
Living area of house (850 sq. ft.)	
times 3 =	2550
Kitchen appliances (one circuit)	1500
Range	8000
Water Heater	1500
Space heating/air conditioning	
(smaller use not counted)	3500
Pump	300
Total load	17,350
Amount at 100 percent	10,000
Amount at 40 percent	2,940
** Net load**	12,940

Since a 60-ampere service will handle a 13,800-watt electrical load (60 amps× 230 volts=13,800 watts), put that in and you're set. If you plan any future additions to your vacation home — whether of space or of power-using equipment — you'd better install 100-ampere service to begin with. Otherwise you face the eventual problem of having an underpowered vacation retreat.

The 80-percent rule for electric motors applies only to figuring circuit capacity, not to figuring total house load. Forget it in making those latter calculations.

INSTALLING THE WIRING

Only when you know how much power you're going to need can you start providing for it. In wiring a vacation house you must start from the utility pole.

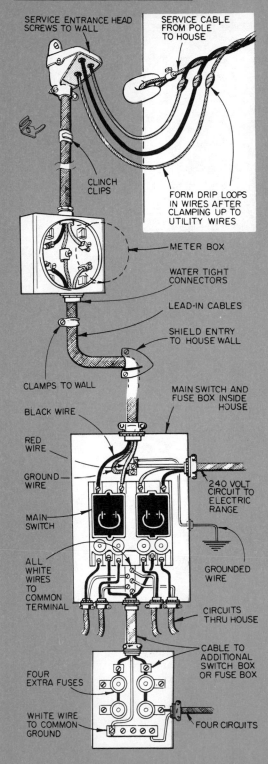

ENTRANCE WIRING USING FLEXIBLE CABLE

SERVICE ENTRANCE HEAD SCREWS TO WALL

SERVICE CABLE FROM POLE TO HOUSE

CLINCH CLIPS

FORM DRIP LOOPS IN WIRES AFTER CLAMPING UP TO UTILITY WIRES

METER BOX

WATER TIGHT CONNECTORS

LEAD-IN CABLES

SHIELD ENTRY TO HOUSE WALL

CLAMPS TO WALL

BLACK WIRE

RED WIRE

GROUND WIRE

MAIN SWITCH

ALL WHITE WIRES TO COMMON TERMINAL

FOUR EXTRA FUSES

WHITE WIRE TO COMMON GROUND

MAIN SWITCH AND FUSE BOX INSIDE HOUSE

240 VOLT CIRCUIT TO ELECTRIC RANGE

GROUNDED WIRE

CIRCUITS THRU HOUSE

CABLE TO ADDITIONAL SWITCH BOX OR FUSE BOX

FOUR CIRCUITS

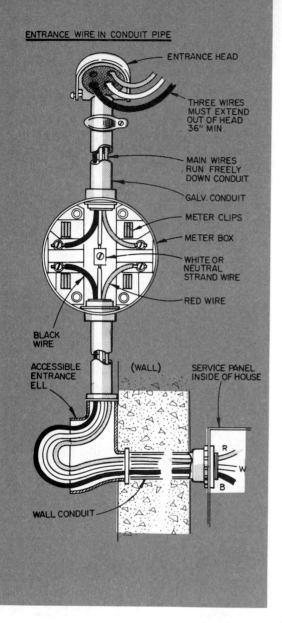

ENTRANCE WIRE IN CONDUIT PIPE

ENTRANCE HEAD

THREE WIRES
MUST EXTEND
OUT OF HEAD
36" MIN.

MAIN WIRES
RUN FREELY
DOWN CONDUIT

GALV. CONDUIT

METER CLIPS

METER BOX

WHITE OR
NEUTRAL
STRAND WIRE

RED WIRE

BLACK
WIRE

ACCESSIBLE
ENTRANCE
ELL

(WALL)

SERVICE PANEL
INSIDE OF HOUSE

WALL CONDUIT

you on what you must furnish to get a service hookup. One common policy is that you furnish everything to the top of the pole, including three feet of extra wire for the hookup. You install only the wiring up to the pole. You do nothing on the pole. It belongs to the utility. If in-between poles are needed, you must install them. You must furnish and install the lead-in wires, drip loops, entrance head, entrance wiring, meter socket and service panel. When your installation has been inspected and approved by the power company, they will complete the hookup at their pole and install the electric meter. From then on, as long as you pay your bill, the power company doesn't worry much about you.

ENTRANCE WIRING

Highly recommended for a vacation home hookup is underground entrance wiring. The entrance wires usually come down the pole in nonmetallic conduit (ask your power company rep). Non-metallic keeps the lineman from touching a ground while he works the pole. Above head height, rigid steel conduit begins. It bends gently away from the pole at least 18 inches below ground. At that point a bushing is screwed onto the conduit end to protect the wires from the sharp edge. The wires snake through a trench to your cabin.

Use Type RHW rubber-insulated wire of the proper size (see table). The neutral wire should be bare and may be two sizes smaller than the "hot" wires unless your code prohibits that. The long buried length of bare neutral makes an unbeatable ground for the whole electrical system.

At the cabin, the wires enter a length of rigid conduit (again with bushing installed). The conduit curves up out of the trench and goes into the meter socket. A sliding connection using two sizes of rigid conduit permits some up-and-down movement caused by settling and frost action without putting a strain on the wires.

An overhead installation uses wires fastened to insulators screwed into poles

If there isn't any service, you'll have to contact the utility about bringing some in. Often you must share the cost of this. You may be paid back later as others tap into the lines you helped pay for. In some cases, you may prefer to provide your own power at an out-of-the-way homesite. This is done with a self-contained electric power plant. See the chapter covering these in more detail.

The utility company rep will advise

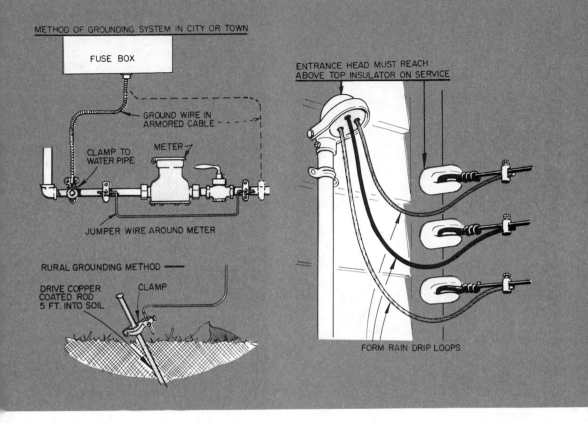

METHOD OF GROUNDING SYSTEM IN CITY OR TOWN

FUSE BOX

GROUND WIRE IN ARMORED CABLE

CLAMP TO WATER PIPE

METER

JUMPER WIRE AROUND METER

RURAL GROUNDING METHOD

DRIVE COPPER COATED ROD 5 FT. INTO SOIL

CLAMP

ENTRANCE HEAD MUST REACH ABOVE TOP INSULATOR ON SERVICE

FORM RAIN DRIP LOOPS

and to the house. The wires should clear the ground by at least 8 feet, driveways by 12 feet. The entrance head should be at least 10 feet above the ground. If no point on your cabin is this high, you'll have to install a mast securely to the framing. Sturdy metal masts are available with flashing that allows them to extend through the roof.

Size the entrance wires according to the table in this chapter. Long entrance runs — over 100 feet — call for larger wires. For instance, a run that No. 6 wire could serve under 75 feet would need No. 0 wire for a 400-foot distance. Ask your power company to figure your wire size if the run is long.

LOAD REQUIREMENTS

Wires the same size as the entrance wires run from the meter socket to the service panel. Choose the service panel of a rating to suit your load requirements.

You can get either flush-mounting or surface-mounting types. The best ones are equipped for all-circuit-breaker operation.

Normally the service panel is placed as near as practical to the service entrance. The idea is to keep runs of heavy wire short.

Entrance wiring in and on the house must be installed in conduit or entrance cable. It is made by gathering up the bare strands around the outside of the cable and twisting them to form a third wire.

Screw terminals on the service panel permit solderless hookup of the heavy wiring. Most will accept copper or aluminum wires. Hook the two "hot" wires — for 240-volt service — to the power terminals of the panel.

The neutral wire should be connected to the grounding terminal. Then that terminal should be connected to a good ground, such as a buried metal water pipe or an 8-foot-long, ½-inch-diameter

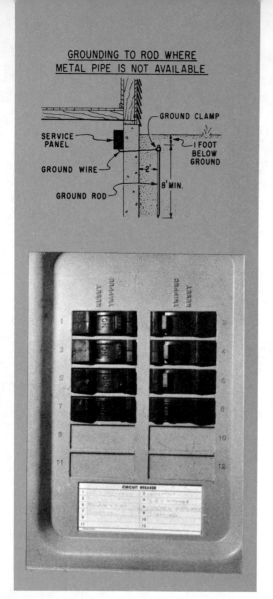

GROUNDING TO ROD WHERE
METAL PIPE IS NOT AVAILABLE

GROUND CLAMP

SERVICE
PANEL

I FOOT
BELOW
GROUND

GROUND WIRE

2'

8' MIN.

GROUND ROD

This service panel has ample space for new circuit breakers. A branch panel here is not needed. Four more breakers can be installed.

White wires entering service panel are wired to neutral strip at bottom or to one side. Try to make neat soldier-like arrangements.

or larger copper-plated rod driven into the ground at least 2 feet beyond the cabin's foundation. A ¾-inch galvanized pipe 8 feet long driven into the ground will serve as a ground, too. Either one should be driven a foot below the surface. Make connections to the ground rod with noncorroding pressure-type grounding clamps. The grounding wire may be No. 6 or No. 4 copper and may be exposed. If you use a No. 8 grounding wire, it should be armored.

WIRING ENTRANCE PANEL

Strip the outside insulation from enough entrance cable to let three feet of wires extend from the entrance head. This gives room for attaching them to the incoming service wires from the pole. Make drip loops and connect each wire with a split-bolt connector.

Use watertight connections between the entrance cable and the meter socket. The connection to the service panel, if it's inside, can be made with a regular entrance cable connector. Anchor the cable every four feet with cable straps. A conduit entrance installation may be used instead, but it's more work. Use it if you must.

Service panels are either parallel-wired or series-wired. The series-wired ones allow the main disconnect to control power to all circuits. Ask your power company rep which you must use.

Many fused service panels have a main disconnect block on the left and a range disconnect block on the right. Both are fused with cartridge fuses. The fuse in the main block should be sized to the rated capacity of the entrance service, 60-amp, 100-amp, or whatever. The range block, if a range is used, should be fused to suit the amperage of the range. The range is wired from the two lugs above its block, plus a neutral terminal at the top of the panel.

When either pull-out block is out or is installed in its *off* position, power through it is shut off. As soon as the power company wires your service to the pole and installs your meter, the two wires from the meter that enter the top of

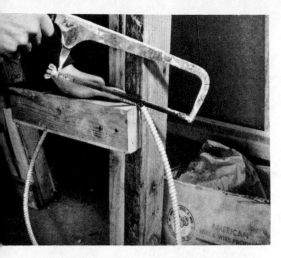

Easy way to cut, strip armored cable is to nail piece of 2 x 4 to stud at convenient sawing height. Cable is anchored while you cut.

Keep cutouts in finished wall close to box so switch or receptacle cover will hide them. Plaster ears also hold device in position.

your service panel are "hot." Be sure to keep away from them. In fact, whenever you work on the panel from the time your power is connected outside, stand on an insulated surface—a dry board if the floor is concrete. The main pull-out block should be removed or installed in the *off* position, of course, until all your circuits are wired and the service panel cover is put on.

WIRING CIRCUITS

Most homes have spare space in the service panel for adding new circuits. Circuit breaker panel covers will probably have some of their knockout still intact. You can install the new circuit breakers in these spaces. Fused panels may have spare fuse sockets. You can get special half-thick circuit breakers that fit two to a knockout. This lets you add new circuits without adding a branch panel.

To connect a new circuit, turn off the main power and remove the screws that hold the panel cover on. Bring the circuit cable to the service panel and strip off enough outer covering to let the wires reach through a spare knockout and around inside the panel to the proper point of hookup. This can take a foot or more of wire. Mount the cable through the knockout with a cable connector. Wire the bare grounding wire to the entrance panel's back with a self-threading sheet metal screw. Scrape off the paint under where the wire will go.

Run the black wire to the spare fuse or breaker terminal and connect it. Run the white wire to a spare terminal on the neutral strip at the bottom of the box and connect it. Make the wire runs inside the box as neatly as you can. It's the mark of an electrician who cares.

CONNECTING WIRES

The other end of the cable should be wired into the first box in the circuit. Cables run between boxes, to connect them in a continuous circuit with the service panel.

Connect bare grounding wires to the back of the boxes at both ends with a screw. Or bend the wires back inside the cable connectors and wrap them around the connector screws before tightening. The box back connection is preferable. The black wires are connected to the brass terminals of every device. White wires are connected to the chrome ter-

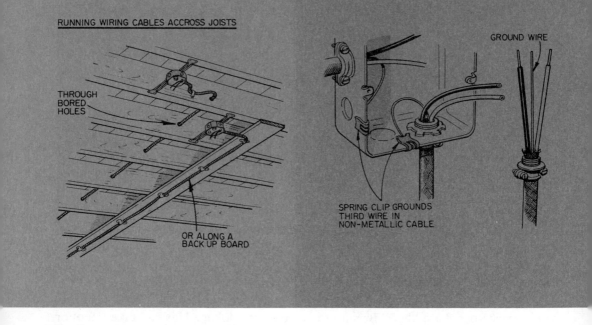

THROUGH BORED HOLES

OR ALONG A BACK UP BOARD

GROUND WIRE

SPRING CLIP GROUNDS THIRD WIRE IN NON-METALLIC CABLE

minals. Never connect the black and white wires together, except in certain switch runs. Then the white wire must be painted black.

If the fuse for the new circuit is left out or the breaker is taped in its off position and everyone is warned, you can turn on the main power after the service panel cover has been replaced.

A cable traverses floors through drilled holes in the wall space between floors. It traverses walls through drilled holes in the studs. Cables can be pulled through ⅝-inch holes. Make each pull before cutting the cable. That way you'll know how long the cable must be to reach from box to box. All splices must be made in a box. None outside. All boxes must be permanently accessible.

Arrange your circuits so that one floor is not served by a single circuit. Then if a fuse blows, the whole floor won't be without light.

In making cable runs remember that three-way switches need three wires in certain runs; four-way switches need some four-wire runs. See the diagrams in the chapter on installing receptacles and switches.

SPECIAL CIRCUITS NEEDED

Heavy-power-consuming appliances, such as ranges and water heaters, need special 240-volt circuits. Three-wire cable should be used. The black wire connects to one fuse or breaker. The red wire connects to another fuse or breaker. The white wire is grounded to the service panel's back at one end and the appliance body at the other. Check your code. Ranges use special receptacles.

If the service panel is wired from the meter using red and black wires, connect the red wire of your circuit cable to the fuse or breaker on the red wire side. Connect the black circuit wire to the fuse or breaker on the black wire side.

If your new wiring will be done in conduit, you may want to lay furring strips across the subflooring so that conduit runs can be made under the finished floor before it is laid. This saves notching of studs for lateral conduit runs.

SPLIT CIRCUITS

Modern receptacles are designed to let you connect each duplex outlet on a different circuit. To do this a three-wire 240-volt circuit is run from the entrance panel. The black wire is fused on the black wired side of the box. The red wire is fused on the red-wired side. In each outlet box the black wires are connected to the brass terminal on one side of the device and the red wires are connected to the brass terminal on the other side. The metal tab between the halves must be broken off with pliers (see photo), electrically disconnecting the two halves of the receptacle. The white wires are connected to one of the chrome terminals. Don't break off the connecting link on the chrome side, or ground continuity will be spoiled.

Another way of dividing the load among receptacles on a three-wire circuit is to alternate use of the black and red wires at every other outlet box. For instance, at the first outlet box connect the black wires to the brass terminal of the receptacle. Simply splice the red wires to each other. At the second box in the split circuit connect the red wires to the brass terminals and simply splice the black wires to each other. Keep going, alternating black and red wires at every other box. The white wires are connected to the chrome terminals at every box. None of the metal tabs between duplex receptacles should be removed for this splitting method.

A third way to split a three-wire, 240-volt circuit for 120-volt use is to carry the three wires only as far as a junction box, near the rooms that are using the circuits. The junction can be made in a receptacle box, if it is large enough. From there take off with a pair of two-wire circuits, each one serving its own set of lights and receptacles. The red and white wires are spliced into one two-wire circuit in the junction box. The black and white wires are spliced into the other two-wire circuit. This will result in all three white wires being spliced together at the junction box. The metal receptacle tabs are left intact with this circuit-splitting method, too.

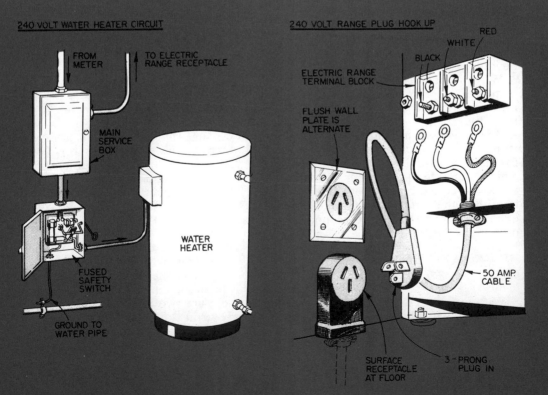

240 VOLT WATER HEATER CIRCUIT

FROM METER
TO ELECTRIC RANGE RECEPTACLE
MAIN SERVICE BOX
FUSED SAFETY SWITCH
WATER HEATER
GROUND TO WATER PIPE

240 VOLT RANGE PLUG HOOK UP

RED
WHITE
BLACK
ELECTRIC RANGE TERMINAL BLOCK
FLUSH WALL PLATE IS ALTERNATE
50 AMP. CABLE
SURFACE RECEPTACLE AT FLOOR
3 - PRONG PLUG IN

WORKSHOP WIRING IMPROVEMENTS

Because your shop uses more power you may need 3 circuits

Light for specific shop tasks is provided nicely with reflector flood in clamp-on photo socket. Shop also needs general illumination.

Your home workshop, whether in the basement, upstairs or garage, presents a special wiring problem. Depending on how many power tools you have, you may need as many as three circuits in the workshop. Ordinarily the shop uses part of a lighting circuit that also serves other lights. It needs an appliance circuit of 20 amperes all its own. Besides this a heavy duty circuit also may be needed for a bench or radial saw, shaper, planer, drill press, lathe or other high-powered shop equipment. If you don't already have these circuits, your shop can be improved electrically.

Why all the circuits? A shop uses lots of power. A ½-hp. motor is all that one ordinary 15-amp circuit can handle efficiently.

Any motors from ⅓ hp. up can benefit from a 240-volt circuit. A power saw, for instance, often has a ¾ or 1 hp. motor. This is wired to run on either 120 or 240 volts. To convert it from one voltage to the other, the wires on the terminal plate inside are merely changed around (see drawing).

HEAVY WIRES NOT NEEDED

With your heavy power tools running on 240 you won't need heavy wires to supply all the power they need. For example, to operate a ¾-hp. you'd need a 20-ampere 120-volt circuit using No. 12 wire. But if you wire the same motor for 240-volt operation, you can run it on a 15-ampere circuit using No. 14 wire. You could run several such tools on a 15-amp circuit, still using No. 14 wire.

Outlets handling 240-volts must have 240-volt receptacles. This is to prevent 120-volt appliances and tools from being used in them. Never use a 120-volt receptacle for 240 volts. Never the opposite, either.

Installing a 240-volt circuit is a little different from wiring a 120-volt one. Tap the power at the entrance panel if there is room for adding two extra breakers or if there are two unused fuse sockets. If these aren't available, you can run a branch panel to your workshop, wiring it to the power takeoff lugs on the entrance panel. Before you do, make sure your service entrance has capacity for the

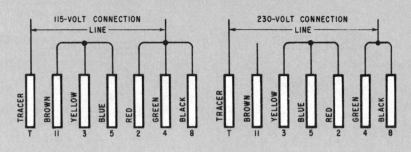

added loading. More on wiring a branch panel is covered in the chapter on home additions and vacation homes.

Normally, 240-volt outlets are wired with three-wire cable. This contains black, white and red wires. The black wire is connected to one of the new circuit breakers. The red wire is connected to the other new circuit breaker. The white wire is connected at one end to the ground strip in the entrance panel and to the grounding terminal of the receptacle at the other end. Codes vary on this point, so check yours before proceeding.

When you convert your heavy power tools to 240-volt operation, be sure to install 240-volt plugs on them.

APPLIANCE CIRCUIT

Generally one 20-ampere appliance circuit will handle all the rest of your shop, provided there aren't more than two ½-hp. motors on it. It should be 120-volt, of course. All outlets must be the three-prong grounding type. If they aren't, make the changeover. Ground the green terminal of every receptacle to the metal outlet box.

Surface-mounted boxes are commonly used in workshops. They mount directly to the basement wall. Hold them in plastic masonry anchors slipped into small drilled holes in the wall. A wood screw does the fastening honors. Duplex receptacle covers go over the outlet, to give it a finished appearance.

There should be an outlet convenient

Handy-boxes with grounding outlets can be placed anywhere in basement shop you need them. Cable, conduit comes from above.

Special 240-volt outlet should be provided for large motors. It accepts only in-line-blade plugs. Motors over ⅓ H.P. need 240.

Handy-boxes easily fasten to the wall with stud-driver or by drilling and using masonry anchors. Anchor cable within a foot of box.

The nameplate on a motor will tell you how many amps it draws. This one takes 12 amps. Use only one such motor per 15-amp circuit.

to every power tool and to the work-bench. A useful improvement could be the installation of a multiple-outlet plug strip on the wall behind your bench. This can be wired or plugged into the nearest existing outlet, or a cable can be brought to it from another outlet.

When figuring how much amperage a circuit with an electric motor should take, double the indicated amperage of the motor. Motors draw much more power when starting. The nameplate lists only amperage draw under normal load.

WORKSHOP LIGHTING

Good lighting in your workshop is more important than anywhere else. There you are exposed to danger whatever you do. Good lighting helps you to see dangers more readily.

Most recommendations for shop lighting call for a sliding ceiling receptacle. The fixture, usually a fluorescent with two 40-watt, 48-inch tubes, or a 150-watt incandescent lamp in a bowl reflector, should be 4 feet above the workbench. The fixture can slide on pipes slipped through eye-bolts in its top.

The only trouble with fluorescent lights in the workshop is that they can, through stroboscopic effect, make moving tools appear stopped. Get around that by lighting each power tool individ-

ually with an incandescent light. Small reflector floods in clamping photo-light sockets work well. If you have sufficient receptacles around the shop, full use of portable lights and tools is assured.

ACKNOWLEDGEMENTS

Appreciation is expressed to the following firms for their help with this book: Adams Electrical Co-Operative; American Home Lighting Institute; Association of Home Appliance Manufacturers; Bryant Electric Company; Dayton Electric Co.; Dyna Technology, Inc.; Electric Heating Association, Inc.; Fasco Industries, Inc.; General Electric Co., News Bureau; Delco Products Div., General Motors Corp.; Harvey Hubbell Inc.; Homelite Div., Textron Corp.; Honeywell Inc.; Hunt Electronics Co.; ITT Wire and Cable Div., International Telephone and Telegraph Corp.; Kaiser Aluminum & Chemical Corp.; Katolight Corp.; Knapp-Monarch; LGM Electronics, Inc.; The Metal Ware Corp.; National Safety Council; P & C Tools Co.; John I. Paulding Co., Inc.; Pioneer Gen-E-Motor Corp.; Plastic Wire & Cable Corp.; Rival Manufacturing Co.; Robbins & Meyers, Inc.; Ronson Corporation; Sears Roebuck and Co.; United States Department of Agriculture, Agricultural Research Service, Agricultural Engineering Research Div.; USDA, Farmers Home Administration; Westinghouse Electric Corporation; and The Wiremold Co.

INDEX

Key: Chapter heads are in capital letters.

Bold face numerals indicate diagrams and charts.